No Way Home

My cousin Margaret.
Sept 2020.

No Way Home

✴

A Novelised Memoir

M S James

Matador
9 Priory Business Park,
Wistow Road, Kibworth Beauchamp,
Leicestershire. LE8 0RX
Tel: 0116 279 2299
Email: books@troubador.co.uk
Web: www.troubador.co.uk/matador
Twitter: @matadorbooks

ISBN 978 1838593 094

British Library Cataloguing in Publication Data.
A catalogue record for this book is available from the British Library.

Printed and bound by CPI Group (UK) Ltd, Croydon, CR0 4YY
Typeset in 11pt Minion Pro by Troubador Publishing Ltd, Leicester, UK

Matador is an imprint of Troubador Publishing Ltd

To Mike, Tom and, of course, Anna.

Getting There

THE VISA OFFICE IN THE BASEMENT OF THE Saudi Embassy in Belgravia was heaving. People of all nationalities, but mainly Arabs, were stuffed into a smallish room, all waving pieces of paper towards the harassed women working behind a grille in the corner. No queue, just a maelstrom of people trying to get to the front. Occasionally someone behind the grille would bark out a name and hand out a passport with a visa stamped inside. Being a smallish woman, I thought my best tactic would be to squirm my way through to the grille. I handed in my completed form and passport and requested that it be posted back. 'You will do that?'

'Yes.'

'You are sure it will be done quickly? I fly to Saudi very soon.'

'Yes,' she sighed, 'no problem.' I was to learn in the months ahead that 'No Problem' was a fobbing-off manoeuvre and a good reason to doubt that what was required would happen. I got my passport and visa back the following week but, because it was written in Arabic, I failed to notice that my two small children had not been included on the visa. Big Problem.

My husband, Philip, was already in Saudi working as an architect to build a massive shopping centre in Riyadh. His company were prepared to provide our airfares but could not get visas for the family. Or at least, they said they couldn't. I think it was a cunning ploy to cut their costs by providing Philip with accommodation on a 'bachelor' rather than on a 'family' basis.

However, as luck would have it, I had noticed an advertisement in *The Guardian* for primary school teachers to teach in Riyadh, working in an Islamic school for expatriates. At that time, all Muslim expats had to send their children to a particular school run by an Egyptian couple and were forbidden from sending them to the highly respected British or American schools. I applied for a job stressing my suitability as an experienced teacher at all levels of primary-aged children and, in the following week, made my first visit to the Saudi Embassy for my interview. It was a mass interview with twenty or so teachers in the same room facing the owners of the Riyadh Madrassa. The interviewers fired off questions to the bemused applicants, none of whom had ever experienced this type of interview before.

'Kate Thomas?'

'Yes, that's me.' I waved cheerfully at them.

'You are a primary school teacher? What do you teach?'

'Well, everything. That's what you do in British schools.'

'What age children?'

'All ages,' I lied glibly. 'At the moment I am a supply teacher.' They looked puzzled.

'What is that?' I explained and the woman owner waved her hand dismissively. 'We don't use supply teachers.'

'But I can teach any class all of the time!' I replied before they had a chance to show me the door. The male owner was looking carefully at my application form.

'I see your husband is already in Riyadh? His company will provide airfares to and from Saudi for you and will give you accommodation?'

'Yes, but his company can't provide visas for myself and our two children.'

Another dismissive hand from the woman. 'No Problem. We can give you visas.'

'For all of us? And can the children attend the Madrassa?'

'No Problem.' So that was it. They moved on to the other applicants whilst I pondered on my situation. Did I *want* to work for this outfit? Should I look a gift horse in the mouth? This job seemed to be the only way the whole family was going to be together. And perhaps it would all work out fine.

The following week the job offer arrived. I was to work in the primary sector of the Madrassa, the age of the children to be decided by the headmistress on my arrival, at a salary of 5,500 riyals per month. There would be a two-week break in February at the discretion of the headmistress. A visa application form was included.

So, it was all coming together. Philip told his company the good news that I had managed to get visas and that we would need to move into our own villa in a month's time. Please could the air tickets be bought and sent to me? They professed themselves to be delighted but Philip was convinced that they now considered him to be a deceptively cunning, manipulative so-and-so.

In mid-September I arrived at the check-in for our Saudia flight, non-stop from London to Riyadh, with seven-year-old Jake and three-year-old Anna. Also with us was my mother who had come to see us off. It was my first ever flight so I was filled with a mixture of excitement and anxiety. The check-in was full of assorted Arabs and the odd expat. There were young men modelling themselves on Prince with fulsome curled hair, dark eyes and slim-fit jackets with sleeves artlessly rolled up to the elbow. They were all happy to congregate together, gleefully exchanging greetings. They ignored the queue, such as it was, and took themselves to the front.

'You're not in your country, yet!' my mother told them. 'We queue in England!' They glanced at each other, smirked, but nevertheless sauntered back down the queue. It was a good job that she wasn't coming with us. I'm not sure that she would have fitted in with Saudi sensibilities.

The plane taxied off to the doleful sounds of an Imam praying, I presume, that we would get to our destination,

Allah willing. The flight was endless and very smoky. In the early '80s plane passengers cheerfully puffed away with no regard for others. Anna took herself off to explore the plane. I didn't worry since she couldn't wander far, although a steward did eventually ask me if she was mine and if I could stop her bothering the other passengers. The announcement, seven hours later, that we were about to descend into Riyadh brought about a huge flurry of black garments. My neighbours, a very pleasant Palestinian brother and sister, explained that the women had to cover themselves – heads, faces and bodies – before disembarking. The sister said she would only be putting on a headscarf but I would be OK since I was a Westerner. Well, that was a relief. After seven hours of trepidation, I didn't feel up to coping with any trouble from the authorities. They said they would stay with me until I had found my husband in arrivals. Which was just as well.

After the baggage reclaim, all bags and suitcases had to be opened for inspection. Staff in long white thobes and red-and-white headdresses went through everything looking for anything suspicious. Quantities of alcohol were removed from hopelessly optimistic expats along with all their videos. My videos were taken too, to be examined, although I was told that I could collect them the following week if *Bagpuss* and *Trumpton* had been passed as non-seditious and without erotic content. I suppose some expats tried to smuggle in porn movies masquerading as natural history films.

The final hurdle was to get through security. My new friends asked if I was OK and assured me that it wouldn't

5

be long before I'd be with Philip. The security officer behind the desk looked at my passport, at my visa, at me, at the children and then announced that I would *not* be admitted into Saudi Arabia!

'What are you talking about? Why ever not?' I demanded.

He barked, 'You have no visas for your children. You cannot come in.' My Palestinian friends started to expostulate in Arabic with the security officer. After several minutes of shouting and arm waving he turned to me and said, 'You should not come without the correct visas.'

'If they are in Arabic, how am I supposed to check them?' I replied. He shrugged, as if to say, 'That's your problem.' The red mist descended and I said, 'Right, if that's your attitude, YOU keep them. I have a visa and I am going through to speak to my husband.' I stomped off leaving my poor children in the care of one very irate security officer. Too exhausted by the whole farrago to think straight I entered Saudi in a blind rage. In the distance I could hear the security officer bellowing, 'Madam, come back! Madam, madam! Come back!'

One of my new friends came over and said, 'He says you can take them.' With as much grace as I could muster I took the children and said, 'Thank you. *Shukran.*' He muttered something in Arabic, probably, 'Wait 'til you try to take them out again…' I had no idea that I had been unbelievably lucky to get away with it.

Living in Saudi proved to involve a steep learning curve. The heat! Although it was mid-September it was still hotter than anything I had ever experienced before. The dryness caused your nostrils to shrivel inside as you stepped out of the plane and I quickly learned to take a bottle of water everywhere. Our house was very pleasant but had no garden. On our street, in fact on most Riyadh streets, properties were bounded by high stuccoed walls with metal gates which clanged as people passed through. When the bell rang, we had no idea who was visiting. Between the villa and the high walls was a narrow dusty yard where a few oleanders and a bougainvillea struggled to survive. We were very fortunate that the 'bachelor' villa was next door to ours and had a small swimming pool which proved a godsend for the children. Immediately behind our house was a mosque from where the muezzin called the faithful to prayer five times a day. Very loudly. I am not sure if there was a real muezzin calling or whether it was a recording. The call to prayer was certainly broadcast through a loudspeaker, so loudly that you had to suspend conversation until it had finished. The Friday morning sermons were the worst. The Saudi week ran from Saturday to Friday, Friday being the Sabbath, the seventh day of the week (*Sabah* in Arabic) and the most important for religious worship.

On Friday, this being a day of rest for all expats, we gathered around the pool next door, plopping in occasionally and eating a communal brunch. Brunch was a new concept for me which combined breakfast with lunch and often afternoon tea as well. The children adored this easy access to a pool and soon became confident swimmers. However, we had to endure the Friday prayers sermon, a high-decibel eardrum-busting rant from the Imam over the wall. We had no idea what he was so angry about or who was the object of his tongue-lashing. If he had been able to see the totally immoral scenes of debauchery by our pool he would have gone into an apoplectic rage. Men and women, nearly naked! In mixed company! Our only saving grace was the lack of alcohol, which was difficult to obtain until we learned how to make it ourselves. Funnily enough, Philip and I hardly ever drank in England but being forbidden to do so brought out a hitherto undeveloped rebellious streak.

The villa was pleasantly furnished and bearably cool when the air conditioners were running. These were large metal boxes crudely inserted into the walls of each room with wiring best not examined too closely. They roared into life every fifteen minutes and chugged away until something switched them off. Then you had silence for about five minutes before they roared off again. This was fine during the day but at night, just as you were about to fall asleep, the bedroom conditioner stopped and woke you up and then, as you were dropping off again, would roar back into life. It was like sleeping with a tractor in the room. If you switched the machine off, the heat was suffocating. By September the house had been subjected to four months of fifty degrees' ambient temperature every day. The walls were hot and radiated steadily day and night. We had a basic water heating system which comprised a 'cold' tank on the flat roof of the house and a water heater in the bathroom. The sun heated the cold tank on the roof until the water was too hot to touch. So we switched off the bathroom heater, using it as a supply of coldish, lukewarm water whilst hot water ran from the cold taps. This was fine until you flushed the loo; sitting on a toilet with scalding hot water beneath you was an unnerving sensation.

The street outside had little to commend it. Facing our villa was wasteground which was extensive enough to accommodate three or four more villas. But in every direction were high walls with the ubiquitous metal gates, giving no indication of what sort of houses were behind them. All house roofs, always flat, were decorated with water tanks and television aerials. I worked out a route to get to the supermarket on Airport Street, which was a twenty-minute walk away, but it was so hot that we were exhausted by the time we got there. If you waited until the sun went down it was suddenly dark. Twilight, it would seem, was a European phenomenon. One minute there was a massive glowing orb low down in the sky (which you could actually look at as there was so much dust in the air) and a minute later it was dark! So, entertaining the children was not easy. Philip worked all morning and was supposed to have an afternoon siesta before going back for another stint in the evening. As the shops had an afternoon break as well, he couldn't help much with transport.

However, my most pressing problem was to find the Riyadh Madrassa and get a driver to take me there. Women were not allowed to drive cars and the bus service only covered the main routes. No one knew where the school was or had even heard of it. There was no address, since there were very few street names other than the main thoroughfare through central Riyadh, Airport Street, leading to the airport, and one or two other named streets. People found their way around the city by drawing maps. Every company or household had a post office box at the General Post Office where letters were deposited and collected on a daily basis. I had a PO box number for the school but that gave no indication of where the school was located. Eventually, someone in the office hazarded a guess that it was down towards the old part of Riyadh near the Mismak Fortress.

I then requested the use of a company driver. The Arabian Architectural Company (AAC) employed a number of drivers, either Eritrean or Filipino, who were, by and large, reluctant to ferry me and the children around town. I was to discover that getting a driver to actually turn up as arranged was a major triumph. The Arab and Eritrean drivers were the most intractable. They wouldn't do you any favours unless you had the power to fire them (or at least, unless your husband had). They would casually agree to take you shopping or to school or down to the souk but not materialise when required. 'Hammid [who was AAC No 1 driver, allegedly], please will you take me shopping after prayer time?' '*Insha'allah* (If Allah wills it),' he would reply. 'Is that a yes or a no, Hammid?'

'*Insha'allah.*' Eventually I would try to pin him down. 'Let's assume, Hammid, that Allah is happy for you to drive me. Are you going to come to my house after prayer time?' He would gaze heavenwards casting around for inspiration.

He would smile, shake his head and involuntarily whisper, '*Insha'allah.*'

The Filipino drivers, or Fillies as they were commonly known, were much put-upon by nearly everybody. Filipinos worked in Saudi as accountants, technical support, cleaners and, mostly, as drivers. Some lived in squalid conditions and worked all hours that God sent. AAC housing for their Filipino staff was quite reasonable and located on the other side of the wasteground in front of our villa. The AAC drivers were Angelo and Efren who were more obliging than the others and didn't need Allah to will their participation in the expedition. Efren was a tall, laconic chap who loped about using as little movement as possible. He smiled lazily if you talked to him but said little in response. However, I avoided asking for him since he thought nothing of hawking from the back of his throat and aiming a giant gob of phlegm through the open car window. Sometimes he scored a direct hit on a passing car. I was so annoyed by this activity (though it was much admired by Jake) that I asked Philip to ask him to stop. But it made no difference; he was probably amused by what he regarded as overrefined sensibilities.

Angelo was a gentle man, always smiling in a careworn manner, willing to help if possible and if he could get away from Nadia, the boss's wife who had first call on all of the drivers. Poor Angelo (he was always called Poor Angelo) devoted himself to the greater good of his family. Like most Filipinos, he worked in Saudi to earn enough money to put his family, children, brothers and sisters, nephews and nieces through college. The Fillies were entitled to one paid return journey home per year although Angelo, most years, stayed in Saudi and sent the airfare home to his family. Like many of his compatriots, he wore two watches, one set to Saudi time and the other to Philippines time so that he could imagine what his family was doing at any particular instant. I suppose Jake, Anna and I reminded him of his family and he was happy to take us around. However, if Nadia wanted him, she got first dibs. I don't know at what time he reported for duty in the morning but he was often sitting outside the boss's house in the car until the early hours to take the occupants visiting or to fetch something they wanted. 'It is a sacrifice for my family,' he would say.

'OK, Angelo, we are going to find the Riyadh Madrassa where I have a teaching job.'

'Yes, ma'am,' he replied. I showed him the 'map' and off we went to explore. After a lot of slow searching of downtown Riyadh I eventually spotted a sign saying 'The Riyadh Madrassa'. Bingo! 'Wait here, Angelo. We'll go inside to see if it's the right place. Won't be long.'

The gatekeeper let us in and we crossed the yard to enter a sizeable stuccoed villa. Inside was a large room, almost a hall, furnished with an imposing desk in the far corner and a row of chairs around the perimeter. At the desk sat a suitably imposing woman and around the room sat dozens of assorted Middle Eastern women, some with children. I crossed diagonally to the desk, guessing that the occupant was the headmistress. 'Good morning, I am Kate Thomas. I have been appointed to teach at the Riyadh Madrassa.' I proffered my letter of appointment, which she read slowly. She was a plump, pasty-faced woman dressed in several layers of clothing and with what looked like a tea cosy on her head. She waved the letter in the direction of the chairs opposite and said, 'Please wait.'

We sat and waited. Jake took out his Super Mario toy and quietly amused himself. Anna looked around taking in the scene. Five minutes passed, then ten. From time to time women dressed in much the same way as the head, all topped off with tea cosy toques, brought in glasses of tea for the sitting women or took papers to the head for signing. I was ignored. Eventually I went back to the head.

'I've been waiting some time, will someone be dealing with me soon?'

'You wait, please,' she replied. I went back to my chair and waited.

'Can we go soon?' asked Anna. Jake pressed on with saving Super Mario from danger. I turned to my neighbour. 'Have you been waiting long?'

She smiled wanly. 'Six days.'

'What! Why?'

'That's what you do in this country.'

'And these other women?' I indicated all the others sitting patiently.

'Some have been here for weeks.' For Christ's sake, what kind of establishment was this? Back I went to Madam in the corner, still sat at her desk.

'I'm sorry but I really can't wait any longer. I have my children with me and a driver waiting outside.' She wafted her hand and shrugged. 'I will come back tomorrow and by then perhaps you will have decided where in the school I will be teaching.' I left before the red mist could descend.

The following day I went back again, still with the children in tow, though armed with plenty of books, pencils and activities for them. The head was still at her desk and wished me good morning. 'You will be teaching in the English Medium Sector of the school. Your class will have eighteen six-year-old children. Beautiful children. You will begin this Saturday morning at 8am.'

The wind was taken out of my sails as I grappled with the idea of this sudden entry into the Madrassa life. 'How long is the school day?'

'Eight until twelve thirty, Saturday to Wednesday. We grant you a two-day weekend.'

Praise be to Allah, I thought. 'And what about my children?'

'Your son, he is how old?'

'Seven.'

'Then he must go to the boys' department.'

'My daughter is three.'

'She can go to the kindergarten. The schools are very near to each other.'

'Not here then?'

'No, they are nearby, two streets away. You will see the sign. The kindergarten – a little way.'

'And the boys' school?'

She demurred. It was obviously too complicated to explain. 'You must ask.' But she offered no suggestion from whom I would get an answer.

Once outside I woke Angelo. 'Straight to the office, Angelo, please.'

'Yes, ma'am. It is a good school?'

'No, Angelo, it is a lunatic asylum.'

At AAC Philip looked up from his desk. 'Hi, how did you get on?'

'Well, I've got a job, teaching infants full time. But it is obviously a chaotic set-up and we really can't send Jake there. It would be an experience for him but I am not sure what, if any, education he would get there. We need to find the British School and see if they can take him.'

'OK.' He called around the open-plan office. 'Does anyone know where the British School is?' Someone suggested that it was three blocks west of the Airport Street supermarket.

'Can I hang on to Angelo for a bit longer?'

We went on another trawl around a different part of Riyadh, again with endless wall-lined streets with little to distinguish one block from another. Eventually I spotted a sign proclaiming 'Saudi Arabian International School'. They too had a gateman who let us in. After that, we suddenly found ourselves in a British oasis with children running around, staff clutching bundles of books – the normal hubbub of a normal school.

'Can you direct me to the head's office, please?' I asked a passing teacher.

'Come with me, I'll take you.'

'Has term started long?'

'We started back yesterday. It's a bit of a muddle at the moment; some children turn up out of the blue and we have to fit them in.' She smiled at my two. 'Are you coming to join us?'

'I hope so,' I replied.

The head of the junior department of the SAIS was a pleasant Yorkshire woman who listened to my story and readily agreed to take Jake into the school, but said that we would have to pay a term's fees in advance.

'That's fine. I will bring the cash with me when I bring Jake in the morning – if that's OK?'

It was – and that was a massive problem solved although I didn't know where we would get the money from.

I woke Angelo again. 'Back to the office, Angelo.'

'Yes, ma'am.'

Saudi Arabia ran on cash. They didn't use cheques, and cash cards had only recently been invented but were not used there. People wandered around with huge wads of money, especially on pay day. Everyone knew that everyone else was flush when there was a new moon. The Saudi calendar was lunar and the new moon signalled pay day! This could be hazardous for the unwary; despite the distinct possibility of having a hand removed if caught stealing, there was a huge temptation for the poorly paid guest workers to relieve the better-off of their month's salary.

'Hi, did you get them in?' enquired Philip.

'Jake is going to the SAIS but I decided to keep Anna at the Madrassa kindergarten. If it's awful I'll send her to join Jake. But we need to get some cash by tomorrow morning. They want a term's fees in advance.'

'Right-ho. I'll have a word with Hani; perhaps the company can give me an advance on my salary.' Hani was AAC's Lebanese MD. He was a wily character, an engineer by training but now intent on making the most of Saudi's massive building programme. The enormous profits that could be earned from erecting prestigious projects would see him, eventually, living in great comfort in Belgravia.

Having experienced Philip's calm, efficient professionalism over the previous months, Hani readily found the required sum for the school fees. Another problem solved. It was decided that Philip would drive Jake to school and then drop off Anna and me in the mornings; Angelo would collect us at midday. I was lured into a sense of complacency that all was now sorted.

The Riyadh Madrassa

PHILIP DROPPED US OFF AT THE MADRASSA before taking Jake and a large envelope of cash to the SAIS. The street was beaten earth with no pavements. Since a large number of cars had already arrived to deposit mothers and children, the air was thick with dust. The gateman was standing by the open gate and beamed at me. '*Ahlan!* (Welcome!)' he cried. He was a tall, burly Egyptian wearing the customary white thobe and white skullcap. I asked him for directions to the kindergarten which he pointed out in the next block.

The kindergarten was a large room filled with dark-haired, dark-eyed tots milling about. The exception was Bobby, a blond child, standing in a cot being kissed by his blonde, attentive mother. The only other woman there was dressed in a Pakistani salwar kameez and was encouraging the children to sit at the small tables.

'Hello, I'm Kate Thomas. I am a teacher at the Madrassa and,' indicating Anna, 'this is my daughter. The headmistress said she could attend the kindergarten.'

'I am Mariam. I teach in this department. Welcome.' There was no form-filling, name-taking or other proof required that I was who I purported to be. Anna sat a table and quickly joined in with the activities.

'Hello, I'm Sarah,' said the blonde woman. She could see that I was disconcerted by the informality of Anna's reception. 'Mariam is fine,' she confided, 'she comes from London. She's a qualified infant teacher.' That was a relief. 'I teach English in the secondary department. Where are you?'

'I am in the infant department but I haven't been there yet – this is my first morning.'

'Good luck! But don't worry about your little girl. My Bobby is happy being here.' So with that reassurance, I made my way back to the beaming gateman.

The infant department was a large ramshackle building, the hard, tiled floors and bare walls making the children's voices echo around the building. Egyptian women with long dresses, enveloping robes and tea cosy toques called to them in Arabic, so all seemed to be confusion. Eventually one of the women said, 'You are our new English teacher? Follow me.' We went upstairs to a large, gloomy room furnished with a teacher's desk, pupils' desks and a blackboard. There were no books of any description. The 'windows' were large window-shaped holes in the wall which opened onto an enclosed area which had more holes in the wall to the outside. This area I later discovered was a Purdah area where the women of the house (when the building had housed a family) would have been allowed to view the outside world.

'Where are the books and teaching equipment?' I asked.

'You will work from worksheets that you can print in the print room. There is a print man who can help you. Choose which pages you want to copy and tell him.'

'And what do the children write on and with?'

'The children bring their own pencils and colours and writing books.' I tried to assimilate this appalling state of affairs and smiled bravely.

'I see I have a blackboard.' I indicated the board which was not unlike the one that I had sat before in my primary school thirty years ago.

'Yes, there is the rubber.'

'Chalk?'

'You must buy your own chalk.'

Fine.

'When do the children arrive?'

'I will go get them now.'

My mind was a jumble of trepidation. I had no idea what I was going to do with them for the next few hours. Far too soon, a procession of Arab and Asian women tentatively entered with their wide-eyed children.

I smiled a welcome. 'Please come in. Children, put your jackets over there and sit down at a desk.' One mother came over to me and earnestly asked, 'Will you love my child?' When I hesitated, she repeated, 'Please, I ask you to love my child.' There was a clash of cultures looming.

'Ah, well,' I began, 'we British teachers do not *love* our pupils. We are very *fond* of them but I cannot say I will love your child or any of the others.' She looked distraught. 'But don't worry, I will take great care of all of them.' By this time the children were sitting at desks and their mothers sat on a row of chairs at the back of the room. I walked over to them and said, 'You can go now.' One brave soul said, 'We will stay.'

'No, you can't. You must go home.'

The brave one said, 'I cannot go home. My driver has gone.' The others nodded.

'I am sorry but you cannot stay here. You must wait downstairs and tomorrow go home with your drivers.' There was much consternation and muttering but I eventually bundled them out.

The children watched me carefully to see how this strange woman was going to behave. Shorn of their doting mothers, I had the whip hand, so to speak. I asked them to get their writing books and pencils from their bags; some looked perplexed and others whispered to them what to do. They came up one at a time so that I could write their names on their books and try to fix their unfamiliar names into my brain. It became apparent that some of the children couldn't speak English. So much for being in the English Sector of the Madrassa. Only eight of the eighteen children could communicate with me. Could it get worse? It could and it did but for the rest of the morning we got through with gifted translation from the English speakers and rousing renditions of assorted songs. They were all familiar with 'Old MacDonald' and his farm, which took up a fair amount of time, and they took quickly to 'She'll Be Coming 'Round the Mountain', once I had explained through my translators who 'she' was. One American boy, Ahmad, proved to be a stalwart second-in-command over the coming weeks. He was so bright and able that I relied on him to convey my instructions to the others. One charming Egyptian girl had a pronounced Irish accent. Her parents had been doctors in Cork so she found Arabia as foreign as I did.

'Ah, sure, 'tis so,' she would comment.

There was a short mid-morning break when the children played in the yard and the teachers stood in huddles watching them. I was the only European teacher. Judging by the tea cosy headgear, most of the staff were Egyptian though one Indian-looking woman turned out to be from Sri Lanka. She was very jolly and introduced me to the others. They smiled politely but were reserved. I asked where the print room was and the Jolly Teacher, Aisha, showed me the way.

'You must choose which pages you want from the master copy and tell Mr Sayyid how many copies to make. If you ask him today they will be ready for the morning.' Photocopiers hadn't yet arrived at the Madrassa so Mr Sayyid printed with a Gestetner machine which smelt strongly of a chemical and the prints came out purple. However, it was better than nothing. Churning the prints out was a simple operation but only Mr Sayyid was allowed to operate the machine.

'That is not work for womens,' he told me. From then on, I visited him daily and put in my order. It was a good place to meet up with the other British 'womens' who were in the junior and senior departments. Some were old hands and were well used to the cunning wiles of the Madrassa management. Most of them were also dependent on the regime for providing housing and flights home. 'Get your request for an exit visa in early for the mid-year break,' I was advised. 'They will come up with all sorts of reasons not to give you one.'

'Why not?'

'They think you won't come back.'

I was astounded, in my first week, to be told that I had to hand in my passport to the Madrassa for the duration. 'Why?' I asked with some indignation.

'That is the requirement of the authorities.'

'What happens if I need to go home?'

'You cannot leave Saudi Arabia unless you have an exit visa and we will not give you one unless you have fulfilled your contract.' Ye gods! I was now a prisoner in this country. When I checked with Philip he concurred. His passport was held by AAC. 'Apparently some foreign workers had previously left the country without settling their utility bills and one chap actually emptied the company safe and took a suitcase full of riyals with him. So now you have to get everything signed off by your employer before you can get an exit visa.'

'What about visitors and tourists?' I wondered.

'There aren't any. All foreigners are here to work or are members of a worker's family.'

'Or visiting Mecca on pilgrimage?'

'Yes, but I think you have to get a special visa for that.'

On my way to the print room one day, I spotted a large electric keyboard tucked into one of the rooms. That would be really useful in our singing sessions. I tracked down the mistress-in-charge of the infant department to ask if the keyboard could be taken to my classroom.

She looked amused and smilingly told me it was only used in special circumstances.

'Like when?'

'When we have important guests. It is not for teachers to use.' It was always one step forward, two steps back at the Madrassa.

Later, at home, I asked Philip, 'Where can I lay my hands on a guitar?' I explained the keyboard situation; a guitar would do just as well, although my guitar-playing skills were not up to much.

'There may be one over at the Fillies' villa. Ask Angelo if there is one you can borrow.'

The following day when Angelo collected us from school I could see a guitar in the back of his car.

'Oh, well done, Angelo! Where did you find it?'

'At the villa, ma'am. Rick, the accountant, left it when he went home.' It was a well-worn instrument but had its full complement of strings. I tuned it up that evening and practised a few chords. The children would be thrilled to sing with it.

The following morning, after the serious stuff of number bonds and writing and learning alphabet sounds, we had mid-morning break and then a fun session of singing accompanied by my newly acquired guitar. The children loved it and the sound of our music-making echoed around the building. At the end of the morning, as the mothers came into the classroom to collect their children, they were followed by the mistress-in-charge. She stood waiting impassively until the last child had gone.

'You must not play this guitar,' she said, indicating the offending instrument.

I always started these conversations with a pleasant smile and tried to keep it going as long as possible.

'Why not?'

'It is not Islamic.'

I stared at her incredulously. 'A keyboard is Islamic but a guitar is not?'

'Yes.'

I pressed her. 'It says so in the Koran?'

She inclined her head but wasn't prepared to give me chapter and verse.

'I have seen instruments like guitars being played on Saudi television.'

A steely glint came into her eyes. 'Please, you will not play.' And with that she departed.

Perhaps there had been complaints from the classrooms either side of mine? Perhaps she didn't want this fun to contaminate the ethos of the school? The classes next door were conducted in Arabic; the children sat on chairs around the perimeter of the room and loudly recited the Koran pretty much most of the time. So much so, that I began to pick up sizeable chunks of the Koran in the ensuing weeks, simply by passing by. Rousing renditions of 'Old MacDonald' must have been a trial to them.

I hurried off to the kindergarten to collect Anna. 'Mariam, can I ask you something? Would you say playing a guitar is anti-Islamic?' A wary expression came across her face.

'People say different things,' she replied. 'In England, no problem, but here...' She made a non-committal gesture.

However, I had the guitar and the children liked singing with it, so I would carry on for the time being. But gradually I stopped. Carrying the guitar back and forth every day was a bother and I didn't dare leave it overnight in case it 'walked'.

Nevertheless, I was a hit with the parents. One day the doctor-mother who had worked in Ireland confided to me how relieved she was that her daughter was being taught by a qualified British teacher. 'They forced us to put her into the Madrassa. We wanted to send her to the British School but they said that since we are Muslim, we must send her here.' She looked despairingly around the classroom.

'Yes,' I agreed, 'it is run on a shoestring. Except for worksheets, we have nothing. I am surprised that so many in my class don't speak English. This class is supposed to be for native English speakers.'

She laughed and explained, 'The non-English-speaking parents want their children to speak English and have a British teacher, so they pay more money! They pay double to be in your class.'

I was dumbfounded but also pleased. The school might take exception to the way I taught but I was a good source of revenue. I would bear it in mind during my next altercation with the mistress-in-charge. Gradually, I became more accustomed to their oddities. I think that they were always wary of me and the other British staff who would always stand their ground when confronted by pointless bureaucracy. The children were sweeties, very bright and happy to learn. I desperately wanted some reading books for them but the local bookshops had nothing suitable. I knew where I could get some but they were 3000 miles away. The village school in England where I taught previously had recently changed its reading scheme. Out went Peter and Jane (and Pat the dog) and a new up-to-date scheme was brought in. I decided to write to my previous head and ask him to keep the books until February when I could collect them on my mid-year break.

Weeks passed and a routine developed. But the vagaries of Arab ways of doing things often caught us out. One morning, the street where the Madrassa was located was oddly silent. No cars dropping off children, no mini dust storm from the churned-up earth street, no indication as to what had happened. 'It is Saturday today?' I checked with Philip. 'Normal school day?'

'Yep.'

The smiling gatekeeper waved. '*Ahlan!*'

'Why is there no school today?'

'We are praying for rain!'

'What, the whole country?'

'Yes. Rain will come. Allah loves us very much. He will send rain.'

'Why was I not told?'

'It was on television last night. No work! Pray!'

'Well, Allah must love the Irish very much. It rains non-stop there.'

The British School was open (the staff had seen rain predicted on the weather forecast and had not felt that their prayers were needed). Jake was dropped off and in due course so were Anna and I.

Rain was not the only climatic hindrance to our working lives. One morning I woke to find our bedroom bathed in an eerie orange light. I walked into the sitting room and all was orange, particularly the furniture, which was covered in a layer of orange dust. Weird. I peered out of the front door to see a fog of orange talcum powder suspended in the air. 'My God! It's the End of the World.'

I ran to the bedroom. 'Philip! Come quick! Something strange is happening!' He staggered out of bed noting the panic in my voice and quickly joined me by the front door.

'It's a sandstorm. The wind has whipped up the sand into a massive cloud and dumped it on Riyadh.'

'Why is it orange?'

'The sand dunes at Ghat Ghat are orange. The storm probably came from that direction. There won't be much happening today, it takes several days to clear it up.'

'Hmm,' I grumbled. 'It's going to take me all day to hoover up the orange talc in the villa.' I hoped that someone at the Madrassa would clear up my classroom for the following day, but I didn't bank on it.

My next confrontation with the mistress-in-charge was over my supportive role for the British staff in the other two departments. She stopped me on the way to the print room one breaktime to inform me that I must cover my face when visiting Mr Sayyid.

'Why?' I didn't smile. It didn't seem to make any difference to the outcome of conversation.

'He must not see your face. It is against our custom.'

'He has been seeing my face since I started working here. It is a perfectly normal working relationship. I don't hang around talking to him. I go in, give him my order and leave.'

The mistress-in-charge looked pained and said, 'Please,' and left. What to do? Another arbitrary diktat from On High which would make life in the school more unpleasant. However, I didn't have a scarf or veil with me so I pressed on to the print room. There was a huddle of disaffected British staff outside Mr Sayyid's hut, all in a state of agitation.

They couldn't wait to tell me of the new imposition. 'Confounded cheek. They have no right to inflict their views and restrictions on us,' said their spokeswoman, Sue, who had already been at the Madrassa for a year or so. 'They sit up there in their damned office with nothing much to do except to come up with loony schemes to annoy us.' There was general agreement. 'What are we going to do?' asked one of the others. A thinking moment of silence ensued.

'I know,' said Sue, 'we'll get Mickey Mouse masks from the toy souk and put them on when we go to the print room.' There were shrieks of delight from the others, and agreement.

'I am going to the souk this afternoon,' said Sarah, Bobby's mum. 'I'll buy a stack of them and we can try them out tomorrow!'

I went into the print room where Mr Sayyid gave me an embarrassed smile. No doubt he was feeling awkward about the position in which he had found himself. I am sure he did not mind seeing our faces which, on the whole, were more attractive than those of the Egyptian staff. Perhaps that was the problem. I wondered why the Egyptians I was encountering on a daily basis looked nothing like the elegant sylph-like creatures that one sees in Egyptian paintings of antiquity. At some time in the past the ancient Egyptians, it would seem, were replaced by the current hefty types that are to be seen in most North African countries. 'Can you print these for me, please?' I asked as demurely as I knew how.

'Of course, ma'am. They will be ready *bukrah inshaallah* (tomorrow if Allah wills it).' I smiled and said, '*Bukrah inshaallah.*'

It so happened that I had no need to collect my prints the next day as Aisha offered to collect them for me. The following two days were the weekend so my opportunity to wear my Mickey Mouse mask was delayed. By the time I was ready to don it, the storm in this particular teacup was over. The mistress-in-charge came up to me at breaktime and said, 'You do not need to cover your face in the print room. We are giving you concession.' She spoke as if a great benefit had been granted and waited for my grateful thanks.

'I am glad to hear that,' I smiled. I couldn't wait to hear from Sue how the Mickey Mouse protest had gone.

Before I went to Saudi I had thought that the British were pretty normal people. Having seen them in action, working in an alien environment, I began to see that they are all paid-up members of The Awkward Squad. They pride themselves on their professionalism and generally work hard to make things succeed. But they take a dim view of authoritarian high-handedness and kick up rough when being put upon. However, the Madrassa still felt it was worthwhile to issue the occasional edict.

School life fell into a routine; the children worked well and were eager to learn. I was evidently making an impression on them, though not in every way that I had been aware of. Having given a boy (Palestinian and a non-English speaker) a pleasing row of ticks for his number work, he beamed and said, 'Jolly good!' I hadn't realised how often I said it.

Every morning I switched on the classroom lights and the dreaded overhead fan with its long swishing blades. I was convinced that it would one day come loose and decapitate the children below. But leaving it off made the room insufferably hot. Health and safety considerations were alien to the Madrassa and probably to the whole of Saudi Arabia. I went to call at the classroom of one of the Egyptian teachers one day; the room was one of a series of outhouses that had probably accommodated servants before the building became a school. Try as I might, I couldn't open the door. I could hear a class inside but no one came to open the door. I spoke to the teacher at breaktime. 'I came to visit you earlier but I couldn't open your door.'

'No, it is locked.'

'Couldn't you unlock it?'

'No, they lock it from the outside. One day a child ran away from the class so now they lock us in.'

I was both appalled and angry. 'What would happen if there was a fire? There are bars on your window so you couldn't get out.' She shrugged but didn't reply. She was obviously resigned to her fate.

On a visit to the junior department, I was startled to see electrical contraptions plugged into every power point along the corridor. Lengths of cable ended in coiled electrical heating elements that rested in a glass of scalding tea. At times the corridor must have been crowded with young children. Obviously, Middle Eastern children had learnt from an early age to avoid these lethal gadgets.

At the end of the corridor stood the mistress-in-charge, surrounded by her Egyptian staff all holding parcels of blue fabric. Spotting me, she broke off her conversation to say, 'Mrs Kate. You are to wear a uniform. This is the materials; you make the uniform. We will take the cost of the materials from your salary.'

I looked at her with a degree of admiration. You had to hand it to them. The administration had an infinite capacity for coming up with crap ideas.

'Children wear uniforms,' I replied. 'Teachers do not wear uniforms. I am not going to wear a uniform. I wear a full-length skirt, I cover my arms, I wear an abaya [which looks like a flimsy academic gown] when I visit the print room. That is enough. Do *not* take money from my salary.' I made a horizontal gesture with my hand signifying that was an end to it. The other staff stared at the ground looking embarrassed and the mistress-in-charge looked furious. If the Madrassa was going to insist, it would have a strike on its hands.

Much to my surprise, no more was said about teachers' uniforms. Some of the Egyptian staff eventually appeared in blue gowns but others didn't. No doubt another black mark had been put against my name.

There were a few fairly indolent school cleaners who wandered around with buckets of water that they sloshed around the tiled floors with a mop. One morning I was glad to see them working with unaccustomed energy. Even the not-so-odoriferous *hammams* (toilets) were being given a good clean. The mistress-in-charge came up to me beaming. 'We are to have visit today! A princess! From the Royal Family!'

'Oh, why?'

'The Princess is patron of our school. She wishes to see our school and our beautiful childrens.'

Later, as I was leaving my classroom, the Princess was walking past. She was a tall, slim, attractive girl who smiled shyly at me. The mistress-in-charge was in a high state of excitement. 'This is our teacher from England. She teaches the English-speaking childrens.' I thought it better not to correct her. I proffered my hand and the Princess graciously shook it. '*Ahlan*,' I said. '*Ahlan bik*,' she replied.

Except for one spectacular, memorable evening, this turned out to be the only occasion that I met a Saudi woman. It was strange to be in a country where you had no contact with the natives. Philip met Saudi men through work but not socially. Saudi wives were kept well out of the picture and there were no opportunities to encounter them. I saw them on the streets, in the playgrounds with their children and wandering around supermarkets but they were always fully blacked over. Even their eyes were covered over, although some wore leather face masks with slits to see through.

Anna was content in Mariam's kindergarten. I suppose there was a mixture of nationalities and ethnicities, although Mariam conducted the group in English. She was going through letters of the alphabet and the sounds they make when I arrived one lunchtime, so I sat down for a minute or two before extracting Anna.

'What sound is this?' she asked, holding up a large 'A'. '"A",' they all chorused. '"A" is for…?'

'Apple!' they all replied. She then held up a 'B' and a picture of a bee. '"B" is for…?' 'Cockroach!' they all called back. Well, they would. Hardly any of them had seen a bee but they were all too familiar with those revolting insects that marauded through our homes.

I had never seen one before, but encountered one on my first evening in Saudi. I screamed as it scuttled towards me across the kitchen floor. 'Philip! Help! Kill it!' There was a sickening scrunch as he flattened it into the floor.

'You'll see lots of them. They're everywhere.'

'Where do they come from?'

'Through that drain cover in the middle of the floor.' Apparently, cockroaches infested the sewers and came up for a breath of fresh air via the drain cover. All tiled floors had a central drain so that water could be slopped down after floor cleaning. So the cockroaches had easy access to everyone's villa. The Saudi variety of cockroach had glossy brown bodies like large dates and whirring antennae to locate my position. Whenever I spotted one, it would change direction and scuttle towards me. One morning when Philip put on his shoe, he felt a squirming sensation in his toes. On examination, a couple of brown beasties fell out! Thenceforth we checked our shoes before putting them on. Even now, when handed a box of dates I check for a stowaway. Expats would gleefully tell new arrivals that cockroaches were impervious to radioactive substances and that after the nuclear holocaust there would only be cockroaches living on the planet. This may not be true but they were so horrible that everyone believed it.

Anna and I went out into the super-heated midday sunshine to wait for Angelo. There were no trees to give us shade, only a solitary lamppost. We squashed ourselves into its shade and hoped Angelo wouldn't be hijacked by Nadia. I would have to bring my umbrella back to Saudi after the mid-year break. The summer sun was going to be far worse than this.

The children

J AKE AND ANNA TOOK TO OUR NEW LIFE IN SAUDI
remarkably well. Soon after Jake started at the SAIS,
the school relocated to a large compound north of
Riyadh, some distance into the desert. This made travel
to and from our schools more complicated but since the
Madrassa started and finished earlier than the SAIS, the
school runs were manageable. The new British School
now had a vast hangar building for indoor sports (vital
for the summer term) and two large swimming pools. A
large tarmacked playground accommodated the hundreds
of pupils as they ran around at playtime and enabled
the boys to play football, although it was unforgiving
on the boys' knees. Jake enjoyed going to school, but the
weekends could prove a trial. The pool at the bachelors'
villa was well used but there was only so much swimming

we could indulge in. He needed another lad to play with. Fortunately, a classmate lived around the corner in the next block. Jake took himself to Patrick's apartment or Patrick came to us. Sometimes we would drive out to the sand dunes at Ghat Ghat where the children would run up and tumble down the orange sandy hills. Patrick produced a plastic sledge one weekend and the children had fun sliding down the dunes as if they were in the Alps. The silence and the majesty of the desert was impressive. Some parts of the desert were rocky moonscapes and others, like Ghat Ghat, mile upon mile of undulating orange sand.

Anna was often the object of attention of people in the street or in the souk. I had been told before we went to Saudi that, being a male-dominated country, Jake would get all the attention and Anna would be ignored. It was the other way around. Strangers would pat her head or stroke her face saying, '*Mumtaz* (Beautiful).' Anna had my Irish mother's colouring: pale skin (which nevertheless tanned to a golden colour in the Saudi sun), brown hair and light green eyes. Shopkeepers gave her trinkets and small items from their stalls. She soon became accustomed to being given things as we progressed through the souk, sometimes small carpet samples which she added to the others when we got home. 'Why don't I get presents?' asked her vexed brother. 'I don't know, darling. I'm sure you'll get something soon.' His present turned out to be very extravagant and problematical.

There was a ring at our villa gate one afternoon. On opening it, I was confronted by a young, slim Saudi man dressed in an immaculate white thobe with a red-and-white ghutra (headdress) carefully arranged on his head. His sleeves were rolled up to his elbows and he held out two black, greasy hands.

'Please, I am sorry,' he explained in excellent English, 'my car has broken down and I have tried to fix it. My hands are very dirty. May I come in to wash them?'

'No, I'm afraid that is not possible, my husband is not at home.' By that time I knew this was a watertight excuse for not allowing him into the house. The Saudis kept their women well out of sight and would respect any European woman who refused entry to an unknown person. 'But my son will bring out a bowl of hot water and a towel.' He beamed at me and bowed his head. I shut the gate. He was delving under the bonnet of his car when I opened the gate for Jake to take the bowl of water, soap and towel.

'Jake, bring everything in when the gentleman has finished.' I left them to it, and the gate slightly ajar. After a while, Jake came in but there was another ring on the gate bell. This time our visitor had clean hands but still an affable smile.

'Please, I would like to give your son a present to say thank you.' Jake visibly perked up at this suggestion.

'No, that's quite alright,' I replied. 'There's no need.'

'But it was very kind of your son to help me. Please, I will give him a present.'

'It is normal for us to help people in trouble. There really is no need.' I was beginning to feel out of my depth in this conversation. I knew I must continue to be pleasant and make light of the situation fearing that he might feel insulted and bring down the wrath of Saudi retaliation. I had heard of expats ending up in gaol for making 'anti-Saudi' remarks.

'Mum, can I have a present?' I glared at Jake and pointed to the front door.

Turning to the young man with my hand slowly closing the gate I gave a vague smile and said, 'Goodbye.'

He returned a few days later with another suggestion. '*Marhaba* (Hello). Perhaps I could take your son to the toy store to buy a present?' There was a violent tugging at my skirt by my agitated son. He suspected I was going to turn down his gift once more. If I had been in England I would have said, 'Clear off and leave my son alone.' Alarm bells rang violently in my mind. This young man was very determined to take Jake off in his car, ostensibly to buy him a toy. As it was, all I could do was to reiterate my litany of excuses and insist that we certainly didn't expect gifts for doing what was 'only normal' in our country. There was a lot of 'ow'-ing and chuntering behind me but I held fast until the young man reluctantly departed.

His final visit was about a week later. '*Marhaba*,' he smiled. '*Marhaba*,' I replied. I turned to the children and sent them indoors, though they were both peeking out.

'I have a present for your son. May I give it to him?'

'I am sorry but that is not possible.'

'Will you give it to him?'

'There *really* is no need for a present.'

'Please,' he said as he pressed a small package into my hand.

I gave him another wan smile and shut the gate.

'What have I got?' Jake hardly gave me time to shut the front door. What he got was a disappointment for a seven-year-old boy but it was valuable enough to buy as many toys as he could have desired. The package contained a travel clock made by Cartier of Paris in brown lacquer and gold. It was exquisite and not at all suitable for a child. Jake looked disappointedly at his present so I said, 'Mummy will look after it for you until you are grown up and we'll buy something for you at the weekend.'

'And me too?' chipped in Anna.

At about the same time, Jake lost his pal, Patrick. 'Patrick can't come round to play anymore.'

'Why not?'

'He went to the shop near his house and a Saudi man grabbed him and tried to pull him into his car. His mummy doesn't like living around here anymore. They're moving to a compound.'

I was rooted to the spot and a clammy sweat broke out over my body. Jake had walked up the street numerous times on his own to play at Patrick's apartment. Had this potential abductor been watching my son as well, as he innocently walked the short route to his friend's?

'Is he OK?'

'Yes, but he was frightened.'

I was frightened. I had heard rumours that European children had 'gone missing', never to be found again. I put these rumours down to expat hyperbole but now, perhaps it was true? Had our Saudi visitor been intent on spiriting our son away to heaven-knows-where? I was going to have to be rather more watchful when we went out and the children were strictly forbidden from ever leaving our villa without either Philip or myself. But I was still not careful enough.

The Euro Marché supermarket, which we visited weekly, had perfected the needs of both Saudis and expats and was therefore very popular.

Searching the chiller shelves on one visit, I saw meat in an unrecognisable form – greyish round lumps in a pack of four with a label saying 'Lambs' Eggs'. This was puzzling. The shelf-filler man was busy stacking more packs of 'lambs' eggs' so I asked him what they were. 'Lambs' eggs,' he replied.

I pointed out that 'Lambs (and sheep, for that matter) don't have eggs. Their babies are born as young animals from their mothers.' The shelf-filler thought for a moment. Pointing at the eggs he said, 'They make baby sheeps.'

Ah. The penny dropped. *Those* eggs. The following week the chiller cabinet had more packs of 'lambs' eggs' but this time they were labelled 'Lambs' Balls'. No confusion there.

I was amused by the wine-making aisle. There were bottles and bottles of Rausch red grape juice and white grape juice. Next to them were stacks of bags of sugar, then coils of plastic tubing then packets of yeast. Large plastic tubs were the final requisite for making a supply of highly illegal homemade hooch. I never dared to buy all in one go, fearful that the checkout man was an undercover cop. So, I bought one ingredient per week and then we got brewing.

On our shopping trips to Euro Marché, the children generally wandered about with either myself or Angelo keeping an eye on them. Next to Euro Marché was the acme of shopping experience for Anna, a Hello Kitty emporium. We always paid a visit after the food shopping and she generally departed with some new piece of plastic tat. Soon after the Cartier clock incident, on an expedition to Euro Marché, I bumped into Sarah, her husband and little Bobby. Andrew and I were introduced to each other. 'How are you doing?' I enquired.

'Not so good. We've been burgled!' said Andrew with a grimace. Apparently, thieves had broken into their villa which was on a compound, and that should have made it very difficult for anyone living off-site to break in. 'They helped themselves to gold and silver trinkets and Sarah's clothes! They had riffled through my wardrobe but didn't take anything, just Sarah's.'

'But that's not the worst of it!' Sarah burst in indignantly. 'They bundled up the stolen clothes and threw them back over the villa wall this morning.' With evident irritation she asked, 'I want to know what's wrong with them? I've never been more insulted.'

'Well,' added Andrew, 'we hope that there will be no further repercussions. We called the police, who came to the villa and took our statements. This was before the clothes reappeared. Mid-interview, I suddenly realised that the cupboard behind the detective contained all our booze. I was praying he wouldn't turn around and spot it.'

'The neighbours, all expats, have taken fright and poured all their alcohol down into the sewer in case the police decide to raid the compound.' We all laughed. Sarah looked around. 'Are you here with your family?'

'Yes, Jake is over there with Angelo, our driver, and Anna is...' I was suddenly aware that I hadn't seen her for some while. 'Jake, where is Anna?' We all scanned the shop but no one could see her.

'Perhaps she's gone to Hello Kitty?' suggested Jake.

My heart raced and my brain froze. 'Come on!' cried Andrew and we raced out of the shop into the neighbouring Hello Kitty shop. We both scoured the premises until I spotted Anna absorbed in a basket of pink sparkly merchandise.

'Anna! Whatever are you doing here?' She looked startled and then trembled. She could see how agitated I was.

'I was bored.' Her bottom lip came out and tears began to form.

'Don't cry, darling, but I was very, very worried when I couldn't find you.'

Andrew spoke gently to her. 'You're OK and Mummy is OK but you must never go anywhere without Mummy or Daddy. And if you get separated from them, just stay still until they find you.'

She nodded then added, 'Can I have one of these?' holding up a spangled purse.

'Not now. We've got to finish the shopping and then we'll come back.' With wobbly legs I led her back to the others who were all smiles when they saw her. Angelo and I looked at each other. We knew we had better keep a closer watch on both of them. The spangled purse became Anna's favourite accessory, and she took it everywhere from then on.

Friends

THE EXPAT COMMUNITY WAS FRIENDLY AND welcoming. Nobody had old friends in the Kingdom, so making new ones was vital if you were to stay sane. Our first friends were Archie and Jenny Bevan from Scotland; Archie worked with Philip at AAC and Jenny had somehow contrived to get a backroom job as a secretary in a British avionics company. Jobs for expat women were strictly limited to those in the medical and educational sectors, so that Muslim women could be treated by female doctors, nurses and dentists. Female teachers were needed in schools like the Riyadh Madrassa. Having an unapproved job, Jenny was kept away, out of sight with the other female staff. Archie had the most amazing ability to strike up a friendship at first contact. He had infectious good humour and whenever there was a laughing crowd, Archie was at the centre of it. Jenny was gentle and had a wry sense of humour of her own. She struck up a close bond of friendship with Anna and the two would chat away on our trips out into the desert. It was Archie who introduced us to the Hash House Harriers. The Hash, as it was commonly called, was the local version of an expat tradition that dated back to colonial times when Brits had gathered, originally, at the Hash House, an annexe to the Selangor Club in what is now Malaysia. They would organise runs based on the British 'Paper Chase', when a trail was laid across the countryside for others to follow. Our local trail leaders used flour which showed up nicely against the yellow-brown desert but would in time be blown away. The Riyadh Hash congregated at a predesignated spot, miles into the desert. The directions were difficult to follow until you got used to the shorthand and the sarcasm. 'Drive 50 clicks [miles] along the Dar'iyah road, turning right at the Nedj forest.' The 'forest' turned out to be a lonely acacia tree with only thorny bushes for company. 'Follow the desert track for 10 clicks turning left at the green bath.' Sure enough, some Bedouin shepherds had transported a green bath, redundant from someone's bathroom, and parked it miles from anywhere. I can only surmise that it was intended for watering sheep/goats or camels. Before going to the Middle East, I sometimes wondered at the saying 'sorting the sheep from the goats'. Previously, I couldn't see why there would be any difficulty. However, Arabian sheep and goats looked practically the same and nothing like the British version. After bumping our long-base American sedan through ruts and dried river beds, we would eventually come across the Hash encampment.

As the autumn drew on, the daytime heat was less intense and by mid-afternoon the temperature was quite pleasant, certainly cool enough for us to march across the gullies, wadis and escarpments that the trail leaders had marked out. The runners did the long run and we walkers did a shortened version, all arriving back at the 'car park' at about the same time. Sometimes the terrain consisted of rocky lumps which at first sight looked like newly ploughed land. But it was difficult to walk over, and a wrenched ankle was the likely outcome for anyone not taking enough care. Little Anna's legs often gave out before the end of the walk and Philip would take her on his shoulders. At times we were led up an escarpment which culminated in a magnificent view of desert reaching to the horizon. I was reminded of the story in the New Testament when Satan took Jesus to a high point to show him the world and tempt him with its riches. The silence was all enveloping. No distant rumble of traffic or twittering birds. Just the occasional puff or groan of another walker nearby. Coming from crowded England, I found the desert profoundly soothing and empty of clutter. On one walk, after a couple of rainy days, I saw little rivulets running down through the rocks. Looking closely at the water I was astounded to see that there were tiny creatures swimming about in it. They must have hibernated in the parched soil for months, if not years, since the last rainfall.

Some Hashes culminated in a barbecue put together from contributions from all who had turned up. By the time the barbecues were producing cooked steaks, chicken and sweetcorn, the sun had gone down and we found our way around by the light of the stars and the moon. Travelling back across the desert could be dangerous, and often cars were damaged by plunging down unseen hollows. To preserve our vehicles, several meetings became overnight camps. A bonfire made from wood brought for the purpose, or from found combustible material, lit the encampment. The children adored these desert camps, playing with other children, running around unhindered, toasting marshmallows on the barbecue and staying up way past their normal bedtime.

We borrowed some camp beds which raised us from the ground and we slept under the stars, bundled up in layers of blankets. The desert was very cold during the night and I even resorted to an Egyptian-style tea cosy to keep my head warm. Anna slept on the back seat of the car but the rest of us enjoyed this wonderful experience of sleeping outdoors. The most unexpected and startling aspect was gazing at the stars. I never knew there were so many of them! The sky was almost white with stars and I gazed up from my camp bed wondering how our small planet fitted into the constellation. What was to stop us bumping into another body and hurtling out into the cosmos? It was all a bit worrying. Every time I woke up in the night, the sky was in a different place. The stars seemed to have moved *en bloc* across the heavens. Yes, I knew that it was we who were moving and the stellar rotation was only apparent. But you could understand how, for aeons, humans had thought (and perhaps still do think) that we were the centre of the universe. Moonlight was deeply annoying. It was so bright, it was as though a huge arc light was trained on us and we couldn't switch it off. We were warned to be especially careful of getting up for a nocturnal pee. Scorpions would climb into shoes lying on the ground and would inevitably give you a sting which could not readily be treated. We tucked our shoes in with the blankets and hoped that the venomous creatures couldn't climb.

Through the Hash, we met another couple who became great friends of ours. John McCartney was from West Ham, and was, naturally, a great Hammers fan. His wife, Becky, was a lively, sparky lady who found life a source of great amusement. Their daughter, Claire, was the same age and temperament as Anna so they chummed up instantly. John was head of sales for an international company so his employment 'package' included a spacious villa on the Al Akariya compound outside Riyadh which not only had a café and small shops but a decent-sized swimming pool. The compound was so large that it was even possible to drive around it. Not that you needed to, but if the wives suddenly decided to take to the wheel, they could do so without being arrested. Sometimes I drove in the desert, although I didn't relish being responsible for the inevitable prang. Our poor car took a battering on our forays into the wilderness. We were grateful for the invitations to John and Becky's compound. It was so nice to be in a normal European milieu where women could wear T-shirts and shorts, swim in mixed company and were not hassled by the *Mutawa*, the religious police.

The *Mutawa* were the bane of European women's existence. They took it upon themselves to police the morals of the Saudi citizens but I think they preferred putting us right about our 'lewd' behaviour. They were easy to recognise: light tan cloaks with hoods worn over their thobes; hennaed scrawny beards and harsh barking voices used to frighten the bejesus out of any miscreant. They always carried long, whippy sticks with which to sting the ankles of any Western woman who was not wearing a sufficiently long skirt.

Philip and I were shopping in a glitzy home-furnishing shop (just looking for some more cups, actually) when a *Mutawa* approached Philip.

'Your wife,' he said, pointing his stick at me.

'Yes, can I help you?' Philip enquired.

'She should close the legs.'

Whatever could he mean? It was obvious that my legs were not wide open but firmly side by side.

'She should close the legs!' he barked at Philip who was as perplexed as I was. 'The close not long!'

Ah, so that was the problem. My skirt was too short and I should *clothe* my exposed limbs. The skirt in question was mid-calf and I was wearing my abaya, but nevertheless he thought I looked like a harlot. The interesting aspect of this encounter was that it was Philip who was in trouble, not me. He was the responsible man who had allowed his property to go out incorrectly dressed and it was he who should take the blame. Philip apologised profusely and after another haranguing we were allowed to leave. I was lucky the old brute hadn't used his whip on me.

We now had an alternative to the Hash and enjoyed whole days at Al Akariya as John and Becky's guests. The compound was not unlike a Mediterranean resort, with sunshades and sun loungers, people larking about in the swimming pool and a general ambience of bonhomie. Sitting out on our hosts' patio, waiting for the barbecue to be ready, with a glass of John's homemade red in my hand, I was beginning to think that this was the life – I could get used to it. I usually sat in the same place and always enjoyed the distant view of Riyadh's lights twinkling away.

'That's funny, I can't see Riyadh's lights tonight,' I remarked on one occasion. No sooner had I spoken than we all leapt to our feet, grabbed the children and the food and rushed into the villa. As we slammed the door shut, a sandstorm slammed into the house. The reason I couldn't see the lights was because an approaching sandstorm was blocking them out. The garden furniture was hurled into the air and the barbecue bowled across the lawn. Sand rained down the patio doors and shook them mightily. It was terrifying being *inside* the house. God knows what it was like for those who were caught out in it. Perhaps the locals were forewarned on a weather forecast but since we didn't often watch normal Saudi television (mainly boring and always in Arabic) we had no idea that this sandstorm was approaching.

'The pool's going to be pretty filthy tomorrow,' commented John. 'You had better stay here tonight, this may last for hours. And the roads will be blocked with debris.' The men and children settled down to watch a video whilst Becky and I prepared a meal from the rescued marinated chicken.

Once more, I realised that you had to keep your wits about you to survive in Saudi Arabia.

Entertainment

EXCEPT FOR THE OCCASIONAL RAINY DAYS and sandstorms, the sun always shone. Every day as we went out to the car, Anna would say, 'Nice sunny day, today,' and one of us would reply, 'Yes, darling/ sweetiepie/dumbo, it always is.' As autumn progressed towards winter the temperature became bearable and, eventually, quite pleasant. This made expeditions out to the desert or down to the souk feasible. Entertainment as we know it in Europe was absent from the Kingdom. No cinemas, no theatre, no live music, no shows where men and women could mingle together. The Saudis loved picnics and could be seen *en famille* on patches of grass with their brass coffee pots and bottles of Nissah water. Some took their television set with them and wired it up to their car's electrics. The main roads around town were several lanes wide with grassy central reservations planted with oleanders and palm trees. It was not uncommon to see families picnicking on these central reservations, though how they got to them I couldn't imagine.

Everyone loved visiting the souk. It was in Bat'ha, in old Riyadh, where many buildings, like the Musmak Fortress, were built of adobe, which is, essentially, compressed mud and animal hair. The builders had come up with an ingenious way of preventing rain from washing away the walls. Protruding rain pipes from the flat roofs extended out into the street, well away from the walls of the buildings. Gargoyles serve the same function in many English churches. The souk was an open-air department store; there was the carpet souk, the gold souk, the spice souk and, quite revoltingly, the meat souk which stank of well-ripened mutton. Flies hummed around it, driven crazy by its intoxicating smell. I bought all my long, wraparound skirts at the clothing souk. They were cheap and did the job. Beautifully embroidered tablecloths and bedding imported from the Philippines adorned the household goods souk. In the antiques souk, you could buy old decorated doors from abandoned houses – the Saudis had little regard for their antiques but they were snapped up by the expats. And for an astronomical sum you could purchase a highly decorated and embossed Khanjar, the curved Arab dagger and sheath.

The gold souk was the most fabulous place on God's earth. Stall after stall festooned with bangles and necklaces, rings and tiaras. It quite took my breath away. The Saudi women were great gold investors. One day, the wind blew aside a Saudi woman's abaya and allowed me a glimpse of her gold-encrusted body. Gold was sold by weight so, however intricate the workmanship, each item was priced according to the scales. Prices varied every day, depending on the price on the international market. If you heard that 'the price of gold has fallen' you could expect that everyone would make a trip to the gold souk to snap up a bargain. I bought a necklace and matching bracelet and window-shopped presents for when I returned home. Anna was desperate for some earring studs but hadn't as yet had her ears pierced. I thought that it was an operation best carried out in England. All Arab girls had their ears pierced when they were babies and all wore gold earrings. Nadia told me that her baby's holes had been put in the wrong part of the earlobe so had to be done again. 'She was already crying so two more holes wouldn't make much difference,' she explained.

The spice souk smelt heavenly. You could smell it some distance away as wafts of turmeric, paprika, cardamom and spices I had never heard of drifted towards you. Great mounds of orange, brown, green and yellow spices were displayed on the stalls with garlands of red or green chillies and garlic bulbs hanging from the canopy. It was impossible to leave without buying something.

But my favourite was the carpet souk. Oriental rugs from all parts of the Middle East and Turkey were piled high according to size. Qum, Kayseri, Heriz, Shirvan, Van – names redolent of the woven treasures of the Orient. The Queen of Carpets is generally acknowledged to be the Hereka from the village of that name in Turkey. They are usually made from the finest silk, dyed in the most delicate shades. They are vastly expensive and rarely touch a floor, the proud owner preferring to hang their Hereka in pride of place.

The sellers would spend ages extracting a particular rug from a mountain of others if you said, for instance, you wanted one with a red centre and animals around the border. If you demurred at the price (haggling was part of the fun and I found out how to do it quite by accident) the seller would say, 'You take home. No money. *Mafi falus*. You look in your home. You like, you pay later.' We never did take up the offer, the penalty for being accused of stealing was too awful to risk. Jake and Anna loved to climb up the stacks of carpets. At first we tried to stop them but the carpet sellers would say, 'Please. They are the flowers of the desert. Let them.' So, we did.

On one occasion I went to the carpet souk to buy a runner to place in front of our sofa. A cup of coffee had been spilt onto the carpet and we couldn't get rid of the stain. A rug to cover the coffee patch was required. I found the very thing, a double rug, i.e. two pieces joined by the fringes, that would comfortably cover the problem.

'How much, please?' I didn't want to spend much since it was likely to be spilt on before long.

'Eighty riyal.'

I looked dubious. 'Hmm. Forty?'

'*La*. Seven five'. Eventually we agreed on sixty but instead of rolling it up for me to take away, he produced a large pair of scissors and was about to separate the rugs along the fringe.

'What are you doing? I want it in one piece!'

'That is two rugs. Sixty, sixty-one twenty riyal!'

I was furious. 'Oh, forget it. Keep your poxy carpet,' I told him and I stomped off complaining to the children. The carpet seller ran after me. 'Madam, madam, you take,' he said whilst shoving the contentious rug into my hands.

'Sixty riyals?'

'*Na'am*,' he agreed. So that's how you haggle. You have to be prepared to walk away.

The oriental carpets were often brought into Arabia by pilgrims on their way to Mecca. Selling them to a middleman would cover the cost of their travel and accommodation. Over the months we came to recognise designs from different parts of the Islamic world and their common motifs and to admire the skill and artistry of the women who made them. Men traded and sold them but it was mainly women in small out-of-the-way villages who sat before their looms to weave them.

We knowledgably examined the back of the carpets to count the knots per square inch to give the impression that we weren't complete suckers. Eventually we picked up courage to buy a few.

Hard by the souk was the main central square bounded on one side by the Jamia Friday Mosque. This area attracted large crowds at the weekend. They were mainly Yemeni, Pakistani, Baluchi, or Afghan guest workers who were glad to have some respite from their labouring jobs. They all wore their traditional baggy trousers with long shirts in varying pastel hues. It was an unnerving experience walking through the throng. Although they parted to let you through, they fixed their gaze on your face and stared and stared. They were probably from remote villages where they didn't see their own women's faces and never European ones at such close quarters. I would station the children either side of me and Philip behind so no straying hand could touch me. A pair of reflective sunglasses helped me to look at them without being seen to be looking. The main square, known by the expats as Chop Square, had a dreadful reputation. It was here, after Friday prayers, that people were executed. Rumour had it (and the expat rumour mill was always fully operational) that if European expats were seen in Chop Square when an execution was to take place, they would be corralled by the police up to the front. Condemned men were beheaded and women were stoned to death by the expedient use of a truckload of rocks dumped on the poor unfortunate creatures.

To avoid ever being caught up in this situation we never went to Bat'ha on a Friday.

Once a year it was National Drive Carefully Week. This was a source of wonder and hilarity for the expats. Large platforms were erected at busy intersections, precariously decorated with wrecked cars which made you wonder how the accidents happened. Beneath, by way of explanation, would be a sign saying, 'Do not think whilst driving'. Of course, there were massive jams around each display as drivers would marvel at the wrecks on show. We saw an amazing wreck on the way to school one morning. A lamppost was bent over at ninety degrees at the midpoint. Skewered onto it was a saloon car with the lamppost going in through the front windscreen and out of the back window.

How it had happened was unfathomable. Saudis were often crazy drivers; they would show their irritation at traffic lights by making their cars bounce up and down by some clever manipulation of the drive and brake pedals whilst simultaneously honking their horns. It was comical to see a row of bouncing cars as if on the grid of a racetrack. Quite often when making a 180-degree change of direction at an intersection, they didn't use the lane nearest to the central reservation but the one furthest away. When the lights went 'green' they would scream across three or four lanes in front of the others on the grid, missing being crashed into by microns. Then there were the Bedouin on the desert dual carriageways resolutely driving towards you on your side of the road. Often as not they had a camel in the back of their pickup seated with the blacked-over women of the family. The men in the front, the women with the camel.

The most frightening aspect of this chaotic driving was the absence of car insurance. Being insured was deemed 'anti-Islamic' since, if Allah willed that you crashed and maybe died, then it was not permitted that you should thwart Him. If Allah willed it, you paid for it.

Philip came home one day with news of the King's Camel Race at al Rumahiya, some ninety minutes from Riyadh. Did we want to go? Philip would be on a site visit that day but perhaps Angelo could drive us there. 'Yes!' we all chorused. It sounded fun.

After collecting Jake from the SAIS, we hit the al Rumahiya Road and followed the cars streaming out of Riyadh. The racetrack could be seen miles away, the disturbed sand billowing up into the sky.

There seemed to be an unofficial car park snaking along the perimeter of the racecourse with the owners perched on top of their cars to get a good view. However, there were two large grandstands within the racecourse so we threaded our way between the hundreds of Saudis, Filipinos, Asian and European expats who were shoving their way in through the narrow entrance, which was little more than a gap in the perimeter wire fencing. All was barely controlled frenzy inside. There were animated groups of Saudi men cheering and laughing, all heading for the main grandstand. The desert wind blew red flags advertising Coca Cola which bedecked the area in front of the viewing area. Rows of plush armchairs took centre stage at the front of the stand for, presumably, the honoured guests. Rather plump older men enjoyed this privilege whilst the younger men stood in the stand or wandered about hand in hand until the race was to begin. It was oddly charming to see men holding hands but startling to see them welcome each other with a kiss on the mouth. The King would be arriving to view the races, although not from the stand but from a coach. This was not the horse-drawn version that the Queen uses at Ascot but a tourist-type motor coach which would race around the track after the camels.

The Saudi women, together with expats from all nations, men and women, viewed the races from the other grandstand. This seemed inexplicable. Were the Saudi women deemed to be safer in the company of expat unbelievers rather than with their own menfolk? If so, it was a damning indictment of Islam and the behaviour of its male adherents.

To get a good view, Angelo, the children and I insinuated ourselves into the front of the mob and took stock of what was going on. There was a large number of military chaps nominally keeping order. I think that they may have been members of the mostly Bedouin National Guard since their marching was distinctly erratic. They all wore desert boots (of course), brown fatigues and the obligatory red-and-white headdresses. Their guns were at the ready but I'm not sure whether they were. They were as eager as the rest of us to see what was going on, so several at any one time were looking behind them at the track where the camels were assembling. Another posse of soldiers marched onto the track, each man with a number (written in Arabic) on a card pennant which eventually was to be given to one of the jockeys as they rode to the finishing line. Various members of the military marched up and down in front of us. I was particularly struck by several senior commanders walking along hand in hand. It seemed so incongruous. I was photographing them when, through my viewfinder, I noticed a Bedouin soldier staring directly at me much as though he were an eagle spying a small animal ready to be devoured. He had a hooked nose and penetrating black eyes, his mouth in a disdainful downward slant. I took the camera down and waited for him to come and snatch it out of my hand and grind it into the dust. He continued to watch me until I was distracted by the children. When I glanced back his gaze was focused elsewhere. Phew.

The camel jockeys were young teenagers, dressed in tracksuits or in grubby thobes tucked up into their tracksuit pants. None of the camels were saddled so the jockeys stayed on by gripping the camels' humps and firmly holding the reins. There were thirty or so camels in each race so the men with the numbers, eventually, had their work cut out finding the right jockey for the right position at the finishing line. The race was off! A charging stream of camels thundered past. In quick pursuit was His Majesty the King of Saudi Arabia with the Emir of Kuwait riding shotgun. The track was a mile-long circuit. We could see their progress by the distant clouds of desert sand that were thrown up by the camels and the King's coach. As they entered the home straight the roar from the crowd drowned out the loudspeakers of the race commentary. Somehow, the winner was identified and given the number 1 pennant. He was feted and congratulated by all around him and awarded a sumptuously valuable prize by the King.

When the races were over we made our way back to our car. Waiting for Jake and Angelo to catch up, I was overtaken by a group of young Saudi women, completely blacked over. They excitedly chattered with each other – in English.

'Where are you studying?' said one.

'I'm at Berkeley, majoring in Math. Where are you?'

'I'm at USC studying Economics,' replied the other.

'Hey! We're neighbours! We must meet up when we go back.'

I lifted my slackened jaw off my chest and digested what I had just witnessed. These young, intelligent, educated women cheerfully obliterated themselves in their own country but probably wore considerably less in the Land of the Unbeliever. I could only conclude that the punishment from their families for rebelling would be harsh. Surely, they would make a stand sooner or later? Otherwise, the Kingdom would lose a sizeable number of its educated women. They would vote with their feet.

Mahmud, a young Saudi colleague of Philip's, had announced his engagement to a Saudi doctor, shortly after I arrived in Riyadh. I met him once or twice in the office but not socially. No one had seen his fiancée but, apparently, she was tall, glamorous and a bit of a catch. Much to my surprise, Jenny and I were invited to the wedding celebration. There would be two nuptial feasts, one for the male friends and relations of the groom and one for the bride's party. Neither Philip nor Archie were invited to the men's bash that was to take place the evening before the bride's festivities so Jenny and I were puzzled by our invitation. However, there was no doubt that it would be an exceptional experience, so we readily accepted.

The bride's event was to take place on the following Saturday at ten o'clock.

'Oh dear, that's a shame,' I said. 'I shall be at work.'

'It's at ten o'clock in the *evening*,' Philip replied.

'A wedding at ten o'clock at night!' I exclaimed. 'What a strange time to have a wedding.'

Jenny and I dressed up in our party gear and arranged with Archie that we would be collected soon after midnight. Sunday would be a work day for both of us so we couldn't stay any later. We were dropped off at the Hyatt Hotel and made our way to the ballroom, a vast room ornately decorated with sparkling chandeliers. At the far end was a raised dais with two thrones surrounded by banks of flowers. On one side, on another raised dais, was a band of musicians, all female, who loudly performed a medley of Arab music and sang lustily with frequent bouts of ululation. Drums play a significant part in Saudi music so the racket from the band made it difficult to hear people speak. There were hardly any other Europeans so we were easily identified as being the wives of Mahmud's colleagues. '*Ahlan*! Welcome to the wedding feast!' said an attractive young woman who turned out to be Mahmud's sister, Yasmin.

'Hello, I hope we are not late,' I shouted.

'No, no, nothing will be happening for a while,' she shouted back, but with a slightly embarrassed smile. 'Come with me, you can sit with my friends.' We threaded our way through dozens of circular tables laid with white tablecloths, cups and saucers and bowls of sweets. At each table there were eight or so Arab women, some Saudi and some Egyptian. They were all in festive mood, laughing, chatting and greeting each other. At our table was a party of Egyptian women who had enough English to explain what was happening. They were friendly and made us welcome. Both Jenny and I were startled by the quantity of make-up and ornamentation that was deemed suitable for such an occasion. We were sadly underdressed. All the women wore lamé or spangle-covered dresses. Their faces carried layers of multicoloured make-up and extravagant eyelashes. Their hair was piled up on their heads in wondrous arrangements secured by layers of gold or silver lacquer. We must have looked like pale imitations of womanhood.

We tried to make conversation, or as much as was possible with the drums thundering away nearby. Most of the time we sat with fixed smiles, occasionally checking our watches to see the time. 'I wonder what's the hold-up?' Jenny shouted into my ear. I shrugged. It was all a mystery. From time to time we dipped into the bowl of Polo mints and crunched away. A large lady with a teapot arrived to refill us with cardamom tea which tasted foul. I called out to Yasmin as she wended her way past. 'Hello, we were wondering when the wedding will start?'

Yasmin smiled but said little by way of explanation. 'They are resting,' she replied. This enigmatic remark had to suffice.

'Hmm,' I said to Jenny, 'perhaps someone should point out to Mahmud and his fiancée that there is a crowd of people here waiting for a wedding to happen.' It was now approaching midnight and we were worried that we would miss whatever was going to happen.

'I'll pop out to the front entrance and tell Archie to come back in an hour.' Jenny made her excuses and headed for the door. While she was gone it suddenly dawned on me the reason for the hiatus. How dumb could I get? The happy couple were obviously enjoying conjugal bliss and not resting at all! I had heard of Saudi weddings where the bloodstained sheet of the wedding bed was displayed to the wedding guests as proof of the bride's chastity. I hoped to God we were not in for that treat this evening. No sooner had Jenny returned than a massive commotion started.

The huge double doors at the end of the room were flung open and a cacophony rent the air. The band went into overdrive and the entire body of guests ululated with ear-splitting shrillness. A slow procession entered the ballroom and made its way down the central aisle, led by a small boy dressed in white silk carrying the Koran on a white silk cushion. Mahmud and his wife followed arm in arm, she with a white veil over her face, although you could see her demure expression and lowered lashes. Mahmud wore a slightly embarrassed smile, as well he might, since we all knew what they had been Up To for the past two hours. Flower girls, also dressed in white silk, processed either side of the happy couple. Then an astonishing thing happened. There was a great flurry of black veils throughout the room when the guests covered their faces as Mahmud passed by. How insulting to him. As if he would even look at them with his newly bedded wife on his arm. Being chaste is one thing but to ward off the lustful gaze of a newly married man was taking things to extremes. After he passed by the veils were lowered. Jenny and I raised our eyes to the ceiling. Whatever next?

The bride and groom mounted the dais and sat on their thrones smiling happily at the female photographer and video operator. As with all weddings, the photography component went on forever. But there was nothing to be done except to crunch a few more Polo mints. A side door suddenly opened and there was another flurry of black veils. In came the bride's father and brother who climbed up to the thrones and greeted the couple. More photography and more Polo crunching. Eventually, Yasmin said, 'We go in to eat now!' All Jenny and I wanted to do was go home but that was not possible. 'I'm afraid we can't stay much longer,' I told her with a sad expression.

'No! You must not go, we have a feast ready for the guests!' It was now half past one and neither Jenny nor I could face a large quantity of food. Poor Archie was probably outside sitting on his car bonnet wondering what was holding us up. All the guests filed out of the ballroom through a lobby where the towering wedding cake took pride of place. Mahmud and his wife posed with a long knife resting on the bottom layer. All the diners again covered their faces in case Mahmud glanced in their direction.

The food soon arrived – great plates of rice, lamb and chicken. I put a suggestion of each on my plate but my neighbour was shocked and said, 'You eat! More! Eat! Eat!' Not wanting to offend I put more on but it in no way competed with the mountain of food on her plate. Jenny and I looked at each other and gestured towards the exit. 'Excuse me, *hammam*,' I smiled at my neighbour. She was too busy eating to hold me back so I snuck out, closely followed by Jenny. Archie was still waiting by his car. 'What kept you so long?' he wanted to know.

'It's only just starting! Go *now*! Before Yasmin spots us and calls us back,' Jenny yelled. It was a pity that we couldn't stay to see the full wedding and the feast but we hadn't had the benefit of a preparatory day in bed as had the other guests nor did we have their gargantuan appetites. At least we had been spared the bloody sheet.

The Hash made a Big Thing of Guy Fawkes Night and we were lucky that 5 November fell at a weekend. A huge bonfire was to be lit in the Wadi Hanifah, which was a comfortable distance from Riyadh, not too far away but well away from the normal Saudi picnic area. Everyone loaded their cars with scrap wood as well as camp beds, bedding and food for the barbecue. It was probably going to be the last overnight camp for a while since the nights were becoming too cold to sleep outdoors.

The Wadi Hanifah was a dried river bed where, at some time in history, a river had carved out a valley bordered by high escarpments. This made it relatively sheltered and a favoured place for a Hash camp. On arrival, cars were parked along a lower escarpment which afforded enough shelter for a row of acacia trees to grow and give the Hashers more shelter from the noonday sun. A Bedouin drove through the Wadi in his Datsun pickup with a camel serenely seated in the back. We had passed a Bedouin encampment several miles back so he probably belonged to them. They wouldn't be interested in us and we left them well alone – though it would have been nice to visit a Bedouin tent complex, if only to see how they arranged their living quarters. There were often four or five large tents which were woven from black goat hair and had several sub-divisions for different activities. The black fabric would have made the tents very hot but, no doubt, they had their reasons for making them that way.

A massive bonfire was constructed well away from cars and tents, ready for the evening entertainment. The trail had been laid, so at four o'clock sharp the runners set off and the walkers followed on. We walked mile after mile over what, essentially, looked like moonscape. A Jordanian college friend of Philip's who had watched the moon landings on television with a servant said his man had refused point blank to believe that he was looking at the moon. 'I know that place!' he said. 'I was brought up there. The Americans tell lies!' The silence was almost palpable; no sign of human activity, just emptiness. The Bedouin must be incredibly resilient to survive in such a harsh, pitiless environment. Yet they could probably have taken up an easier life if they had wanted it, given the vast wealth that was now awash in the country.

As night fell, the barbecue was set alight and the cooking began. The chief bonfire maker checked his construction and, much to everyone's delight, pulled a Guy from the boot of his car and carefully clambered up the structure to place a very realistic effigy of Guy Fawkes on top. The Hashers gathered round and enjoyed the heat from the crackling fire and watched the flames licking up to the top. 'Are we going to have fireworks?' asked Jake.

'No, sorry, old chap, you can't get them in Saudi. At least, people like us can't get them,' replied his dad.

'Ow,' said Jake.

The fire would have been seen miles away, probably as far as the Bedouin encampment. I was suddenly aware that a Bedouin shepherd with his flock of sheep/goats had joined the ring of watchers. Someone nearby gave him a glass of Coke and pointed to the fire. '*Kebir* (Big),' he acknowledged. '*Kebir iktir!*'

'A British tradition,' explained the Coke-giver.

The shepherd continued to gaze at the fire. 'Why you burn Saudi?' The Coke-giver stared at the Guy in horror, for sure enough, Guy Fawkes looked a dead ringer for the Saudi he was standing next to. Long dark hair, dark eyes, dark moustache and pointy beard.

'No, no! That's not a Saudi, that's Guy Fawkes. He was English. Bad man. Tried to kill the King of England! We are happy he did not succeed.' The shepherd looked unconvinced and perhaps his English wasn't up to the niceties of British history. Several others joined in with affirmations that the chap on top of the bonfire was a bad Englishman and not a Saudi. It was vital that reports of anti-Saudi behaviour would not be relayed to the authorities. The consequences could be catastrophic for the Hash.

As the fire died down, the shepherd and his flock melted back into the night, hopefully with a positive account of what he had seen.

Festive Greetings

WINTER IN SAUDI WAS RATHER NICE. THE sun still shone most of the time but it was very cold. The winter winds blew down from the Urals making the mornings very fresh. Fortunately, I had packed winter jackets and coats (for our mid-year break) so we could still venture out into the desert, although sleeping out under the stars was over for the time being.

We were fast approaching Christmas so, meeting Sarah in the kindergarten one day, I asked her what arrangements the Madrassa made for the day. She laughed, 'None. They completely ignore it. In fact, you are best advised not to mention the subject. It is just the same as any other day to them. Everyone obliquely refers to Christmas as The Time of Festive Greetings.'

'Oh.' That sounded grim. 'No Christmas cards on sale?'

'No, but if you are quick off the mark there are a limited number of Festive Greetings cards on sale at Al Kitab, the bookshop.'

'So, it's school as usual?'

'Not this year, Christmas falls on a weekend. You can cook a festive meal and pretend you are home. Better still, book yourselves into the Riyadh Marriott for their Festive Greetings lunch. They produce roast turkey with all the trimmings though not Christmas pudding, I'm afraid.'

This sounded more promising. The Marriott Hotel was at the end of our street so we called in on our way home and I made a booking. Al Kitab had a few Festive Greetings cards decorated with camels which I snapped up. At least the family at home would get a card from us.

Buying presents was not a problem other than ensuring the appropriateness of the item; shopping was the Saudis' and expats' favourite pastime. Jake was desperate for a Swiss Army knife which I absolutely refused to let him have. 'Ow' was the usual response. However, he cheered up when a remote-controlled car was suggested as an alternative. Anna lusted after a Spanish flamenco dress with layers of frills and a swirling train. They cost an absolute fortune so I was reluctant to commit such a large sum of money for a garment she would soon grow out of. I still regret not buying her one. Philip and I treated each other to new expensive watches, items we had hitherto been unable to afford.

Earning two substantial tax-free salaries was delightful after years of 'getting by' on English wages. The expat mantra for life in Saudi was 'First year need, second year greed, third year brain damage.' We were still in the first category and our main aim was to save as much money as possible for our future life in the UK, although some expats were seduced by the good salaries and exotic holidays and became perpetual peripatetic nomads, moving around the Middle East, the Far East, Australia and the States. However, a little splurge at Festive Greetings was, in part, a reward for overcoming the challenges of the previous few months. We lived on my salary and sent Philip's home to our English bank every month. The new moon heralded 'Pay Day!' and I indulged in my monthly pastime of Counting the Money. (Our employers, like all others in Saudi, paid salaries in cash only.) Heaps of cash were deposited in piles around our double bed as I allocated how much could be spent on which items. Christmas was going to put a hole in the savings heap but we were due an indulgence. The savings heap was carried to the exchange bank to be converted into a sterling cheque to be posted home. It was my job to enter the lions' den with our wodge of riyals. The bank was crammed with expat workers, mostly third world nationals, all converting their wages into home currencies. If Philip had gone into the bank he would have had to queue up with everyone else but since I was a woman with children in tow (not a common sight in the bank) I was ushered expeditiously to the front. 'Come, come, madam!' called the teller from behind the grille. The men parted like the Red Sea before Moses and it took only minutes to process my business. My grateful husband waited outside in the car relieved of at least one tedious task.

Christmas morning arrived with gleeful cries from Jake. 'Look what Father Christmas gave me!' He stood grinning at the foot of our bed brandishing a Swiss Army knife. '*You* wouldn't buy me one but Father Christmas did! I *knew* he was real!' I turned and stared at Father Christmas on the pillow next to me. It was his job to buy the stocking fillers and he had broken ranks to give Jake his heart's desire. I forced a smile and said, 'You *are* a lucky boy. Though I might have a word with Father Christmas if I ever meet him…' Father Christmas was not so magnanimous to Anna who had found a doll dressed in a Spanish flamenco costume in her stocking rather than the real thing. Obviously, Philip could relate to getting an army knife more than a flouncy frock. Even so, she was happy to get it. The children each enjoyed new remote-controlled cars which they later raced up the road to the Marriott Hotel.

The main dining room was packed with Europeans trying to be as festive as was allowed. 'Happy Christmas,' we daringly greeted one another. The tables were decorated with holly and poinsettias, flown in especially for the occasion, and we all toasted each other with Rausch fizzy grape juice, in lieu of anything more intoxicating. The festive meal was pretty authentic and we shared a collective bonhomie with our fellow sufferers. The background music was the usual anodyne hotel playlist with not a hint of a carol. A grand piano stood nearby and I was desperate to go over and regale the company with renditions of 'God Rest Ye Merry Gentlemen' and 'Silent Night'. But I suspect most of us would have been in tears if

73

I had. And I would probably have spent the rest of the day in the neighbourhood police station.

After Christmas I turned my mind towards the mid-year break and how I was to extract an exit visa from the Madrassa.

Back to Blighty

I KEPT AN EYE OUT FOR THE MISTRESS-IN-CHARGE at the Madrassa. She didn't seem to have an office but floated about checking that all was in order. Aisha thought she might be found in the junior department so whilst my class was receiving their religious instruction I went off to find her. I marvelled yet again at the tea-heating contraptions plugged into the corridor walls and found my quarry indulging in a pleasant chat with one of her minions. When she spotted me advancing towards her, her face assumed a 'What now?' expression.

'*Marhaba, Salaam alleykum,*' I greeted her, showing off my newly acquired Arabic.

'*Wa 'alleykum, as'salaam,*' she replied warily. 'How can I help you, Mrs Kate?'

'Please could you ask the office to process exit visas for myself and my children for the mid-year break?'

'That is not possible,' was her opening gambit.

'Because?'

She smiled condescendingly and replied, 'Visas are only granted in special circumstances.'

'Such as?'

'Ill health...'

'My mother is ill.' We stared at each other both working out our next move. She knew I was lying and I knew she knew I was lying. 'She lives alone and very much wants me and my children to visit her.'

'In London?' I wasn't going to quibble. To most Arabs, the whole of the United Kingdom was London, even Scotland, much to Archie's irritation.

'Yes. When we came in September, the London visa office failed to put my children's visas onto my passport. They are here illegally.' Her eyes popped open wide at this information. 'I would like the Madrassa visa office *to be very careful* in giving us all correct exit and re-entry visas. I don't want to go through the terrible trouble I had at security again, trying to get into Saudi.' Having laid it on pretty thick about getting back into Saudi I think I convinced her that I would return after the break. I decided not to tell her about the reading books that I hoped to bring back with me. She might have been pleased or she might have been insulted that I thought their provision of Gestetner sheets was inadequate.

'Your husband is going also?'

'No, he is happy that we can visit my mother and two weeks away is not very long.'

'I will speak to the office.' And with that, she waddled off. I felt a great sense of achievement.

Two weeks later she presented me with my lovely dark blue passport adorned with purple, green and orange stamps, and rubber-inked stampings also in purple and green for good measure. The stamps were liberally decorated in Arabic handwriting, hopefully including Anna, Jake and myself in the EXIT & RE-ENTRY VISA. 'This says all three of us can go and come back?'

'Yes, yes, of course,' she sighed. There was no 'of course' about it so I delivered it to Philip's office on the way home for the Arab-speaking office manager to check that they had done it right this time. They had. I could now go ahead and book my flights and make another hole in our savings. AAC provided the family with return flights once a year so my mid-year jolly would have to be paid for by us. To cut the cost, I discovered I could get cheap flights with Egyptair flying out of Dhahran on the east coast, flying to London with a stopover in Cairo. *That'll be nice*, I thought. *We might have time to see the Pyramids*. The internal flight from Riyadh to Dhahran wasn't too expensive, making the overall cost considerably less than travelling direct with Saudia, the Saudi national airline.

It occurred to me that perhaps when I was in England I should get individual passports made for the children. If, for any reason, Philip needed to travel to the UK with the children he couldn't go without me since they were both on my passport. To this end I paid a visit to a local photographic shop to have passport photos taken. The results were extraordinary. Anna looked like a little Arab child. It being a black and white photo, Anna's brown hair looked dark but her pale green eyes didn't register as being light coloured. Even Jake, with his sun-bleached blond hair, looked Middle Eastern. For no very good reason I had my photo taken as well and the resulting snap made me look a born and bred Egyptian. With several copies of each I was prepared for a visit to the passport office in England. We wouldn't be able to use the new passports returning to Saudi but we should be able to get exit visas stamped in them for the home visit in the summer.

The days to our departure dragged by. I couldn't wait to go. I paid a visit to the gold souk to buy gifts for my mother and Philip's. Anna chose a pretty pair of stud earrings in the shape of flowers so that if she had her ears pierced in England, she would have earrings ready to wear. A couple of hand-embroidered tablecloths with matching napkins completed my purchases and I started packing. Stupidly, I decided to wear all my gold on the journey home, thinking that it would be safer round my neck than in a suitcase that might be broken into. It was a decision I was to regret.

At last, the children and I set off to the airport with Philip. It was only five months since our arrival and in that time my world had been turned upside down, flattened and put through the wringer. But Saudi hadn't got the better of me – not yet.

We dropped off our baggage, kissed Philip goodbye and set off for Egypt. We hadn't been seated on the internal flight for more than a few minutes when a steward came to enquire if the children wanted to visit the pilots in the cockpit. 'Ooh yes!' said Jake. Anna took his hand and went with him to the front. Minutes later the steward came to ask if I would like to see the cockpit. I readily accepted the invitation and soon found myself at the business end of the plane. The pilots were in their seats ready for take-off and the children were agog at the myriad of dials and switches banked before them.

The chief pilot turned in his seat towards me. 'Your daughter is very beautiful.'

'Thank you,' I smiled.

'I wanted to check the mother, to see how she will grow up,' he continued.

I didn't know what to say to this remark so muttered, 'Oh, um, oh.'

'How much to buy her?'

I stared at him dumbfounded. Had I heard him right?

He repeated, 'How much to buy your daughter?'

He wasn't smiling, he wasn't joking, he was deadly serious. Looking straight into my eyes he brazened out his preposterous question.

'What?!' I demanded. Despite not wanting to offend him, I couldn't stop myself sounding shocked.

Once more, 'How much to buy your daughter?' He continued looking directly into my eyes arrogantly assured that he could ask such a disgusting question.

I did not want us to be thrown off the plane by causing a scene so I restrained myself from shouting at him.

'She is *not* for sale.' My voice was cold and barely hid the revulsion I felt for him. I turned to Jake and Anna. 'Right-oh, you two, back to your seats.' I ushered them out and left without a backward glance. Sitting down, I found I was shaking. 'Did the pilot want to buy Anna?' asked Jake. 'No, of course not, darling. He just has a strange sense of humour.' Anna seemed oblivious of her value as a commodity and chatted away as though nothing untoward had happened. This was a very stark warning that I was in a country where the norms of British behaviour could not be relied upon. I should have heeded the warning and headed home for good.

The rest of the journey to Dhahran and then on to Cairo was, mercifully, uneventful. The Egyptair flight was full of British expats who had been working in the oil fields of the eastern region. They were frequent fliers on this airline and were old hands at demanding the best available accommodation in Cairo. On hearing that we were going to be taken to a particular hotel for the night they started loudly complaining and demanding that it was the 'Novotel or nothing. We're not getting off the coach unless we go to the Novotel.' After a hurried, whispered discussion, the flight representative gave the driver instructions to take us to the Novotel hotel. The Awkward Squad gave a great cheer and peace was restored.

The Novotel was rather nice. Our room had twin king-sized beds and modern fittings. It looked down into a central atrium where a large sparkling pool enticed us for a swim. 'Can we?' asked Jake but we had no swimwear with us and it was rather late. 'No, I'm afraid not but I'm hoping we can take a trip to the Pyramids tomorrow.' Our following flight was not until the next evening so we might be able to get to Giza and back in time. We went to make enquiries and to get some food.

The concierge in the foyer said that one of their preferred taxis, indicating a row of taxis by the entrance, would be very happy to drive us to and from the Pyramids at Giza the following morning. Yes, the driver would wait whilst we visited the site and no, there would be no extra charge. There was a set charge for the trip so I could budget accordingly. I set aside the taxi fare and calculated that I might have enough for a guided trip around the Pyramids and then enough left over for a cup of tea. Some hope.

Straight after breakfast, we made our way to the taxi rank and met our driver for the day. He was not unlike Angelo – a round smiley face and a friendly demeanour. The car quickly took us along the Nile Corniche and then over the great river itself. I had a friend whose preferred dress colour was *eau de Nil* which I thought of as a soft bluey green but that was nothing like the real thing which flowed a sludgy grey beneath us. Our driver said, '*Al Nil,*' pointing at the river.

'The River Nile?' I replied.

'What river?' he asked. '*Al Nil.*'

It suddenly dawned on me that the Arabic for river was *Nil* and we were crossing The River. It had no other name since there was no other river, just as *Sahara* means desert in Arabic. To say Sahara Desert to an Egyptian is to say Desert Desert!

Giza was no longer in the desert, despite the photos you see of the Pyramids. The greatest structures of the ancient world were surrounded by suburban Cairo. The famously pyramidal shapes appeared above the houses of Giza and we found ourselves marvelling at the massive structures far sooner than I had expected.

We got out of the taxi and set off towards the Great Pyramid. Before we had got very far we were assailed by a group of camel drivers who invited us to tour the site on a camel.

'How much?'

'Two camels? One hundred pounds.'

'What?!'

'Egyptian pounds. Good price.'

I looked at my taxi driver who said it was OK. Jake was thrilled at the prospect of a camel ride and I was keen not to have to walk further than necessary in the morning heat. We had never had the chance to ride on a camel in Saudi, even though there were plenty around. Not having a tourist industry, the Saudis didn't see the point of setting up camel trails for the expats. Mounting a camel was interesting. They sat on the ground with their long legs tucked under them so getting up into the saddles with the aid of a pair of steps wasn't too difficult. Jake was on one beast and Anna and I were on the other one. To stand up, the camel raises its *back* legs and hurls the rider forward. Just as you think you are about to hit the dust, it straightens its front legs and hurls you back. This caused great hilarity amongst the camel drivers who, no doubt, got their daily quotient of laughter from watching their unsuspecting customers. We hung on grimly and set off towards the Sphinx on our circumnavigation of the Pyramids. The camels were led by a lad on a donkey so I was fairly confident that the camels wouldn't charge off with us on top.

It is well known that the Pyramids are made from large blocks of stone, but when you are right next to one, you cannot begin to imagine how they were manoeuvred into position. They are so massive that they are as large as houses. The camels plodded around on their well-worn circuit until we arrived back at the Sphinx and made loud roaring grumblings whilst they settled down on the ground. We hung on mightily this time as their legs folded front then aft and we were able to dismount.

I was about to pay for the trip when, 'Madam would like a glass of tea and visit our perfume factory?' enquired the camel owner. The group of drivers grinned at me manically. What possessed me to accept their invitation, I'll never know. They weren't actually looking at me, but rather at the several gold necklaces festooned about my neck. I was obviously Very Rich. We entered the 'perfume factory' which was, essentially, a shed furnished in soft sofas with walls covered in shelving containing bottles and bottles of perfume. A glass of tea was proffered, with sugary soft drinks for the children. The next twenty minutes passed in a blur. Which perfume did I like? Would I like this one? Or perhaps this other one? At regular intervals they somehow abstracted money from me. Even as they did it, I couldn't account for how it was happening. They had perfected the art of fleecing the tourist to the nth degree. Eventually I got a grip, stood up and announced that I was going. 'But, madam, we have more perfumes!'

'You've got ALL my money so there's no point in me being here any longer.' I took each child by the hand and marched them out, tramping off towards the taxi rank. Thank God my driver was still there. The driver stood looking at me anxiously. He feared the worst. 'Madam, I was afraid when you went to the perfume shop.'

'I wish you had warned me about them. They have taken all my money.'

He looked at me aghast. 'All your money?!'

'Well, all of *my* money, not *yours*. I had hidden yours in a secret place.' His face relaxed and he sighed with relief. His money had been folded into my bra so his fare might be somewhat moist but it would be the full amount. 'So, I have nothing more. You had better take us back to the hotel. I might be able to persuade them to give me a cup of tea.'

'I will take you to my home for refreshments,' he smiled. 'My madam is at home. She will give you tea and cakes.' Later, when I was recounting this tale to Philip, he stared at me hard and said that I was completely crackers. 'You actually went with him?'

'Well, we were hungry and thirsty. And penniless.'

The taxi driver took us through the City of the Dead, an area of Cairo composed of large ornate tombs with families gathered around the bases of them. To my amazement, they appeared to be picnicking. The driving in central Cairo was the worst I have ever encountered. Cars from several directions funnelled into one main thoroughfare with no give or take by any of the drivers. They just bellowed obscenities at each other and, with arms outstretched through their windows, hammered violently on neighbouring cars whilst keeping the other hand permanently on the horn. Taking advantage of the stationary traffic, one heavily scarred young man pressed his burned torso against our window and thrust a hand through the driver's window begging for money. It was all ghastly. Eventually, we bumped along an unmade road in the middle of what looked like a building site. There were streets of half-built apartment blocks with rubble and building materials lying around haphazardly. 'This is my apartment,' said our driver with a degree of pride. I thought he was joking. It was clearly a partially built block with no doors or windows. We climbed rubble-filled stairs to the first floor and I thought I had made another bad mistake. But there was a door and, on entering, we found ourselves in an ornately furnished apartment with a very surprised madam sitting at the table with her little baby in her arms. Our driver explained our dilemma to her and in no time at all we were given tea, drinks and a variety of cakes. They were so very friendly and charming. Madam couldn't speak English and my Arabic was still too basic to communicate. But I made cooing noises at the baby and we all smiled a lot.

Thoroughly refreshed, we were taken back to our hotel where I extracted a roll of Egyptian pounds from my 'secret place' and wished our driver all the best. He and his wife had redeemed my hitherto underwhelmed opinion of his countrymen.

Home

ENGLAND IN FEBRUARY WAS DISMAL YET delightful. It was good to be back amongst people who behaved in predictable ways. You could relax knowing that, by and large, people followed the rules, be it queuing at shop counters, them saying sorry when you bumped into them, or chatting about the weather at bus stops. And yet, when one damp day followed another, we missed the bright days and trips out to the desert. My friends wanted to know all about my experiences but it was difficult to explain in a way that fully expressed the strangeness of what I had experienced. Several teacher friends were stunned by the awfulness of the Madrassa and wondered at my resolve to return. 'I have to,' I explained. 'We shan't see Philip until the summer if we don't.'

My mother was thrilled to see me and doted on the children. 'I've missed you so much but it won't be long now. You've done half the year and you'll soon be home for good.' Anna had her arms wrapped around her nana and I could see that having us living far away was a wrench for Mum. Philip and I had discussed staying on for a second year if I could get out of the Madrassa's clutches and get a job at the SAIS. However, I didn't want to cast a cloud over the future and it might not happen.

Philip's parents lived in Peterborough so I combined a visit to them with one to the passport office, which was conveniently in the same part of town. With the forms filled and photos provided, I parted with a substantial fee and was told to return later in the day to collect the new passports.

Philip's parents were delighted to see us. They had lived in the Sudan during the early years of their marriage and Philip had been born in Khartoum. We compared notes on living in a desert country amongst Arabs. They had lived a fairly privileged life, being part of the British-run government, but mod cons had been of a basic design back then in a post-war Middle East. Travel to and from was arduous, with several flights required to get back to England. They marvelled that we could travel in our car across Arabia if we had a mind to. They remembered the sandstorms and sleeping out under the stars. My mother-in-law was very pleased with the gold necklace I had brought back for her although she was alarmed by my tale of carrying it around my neck whilst visiting Giza. 'You could have been robbed!' she said. 'Hmmm,' I replied.

The head of my old school was amused by my need to take the old Ladybird reading scheme back to Saudi. He was glad to get rid of it to a good cause and I was relieved that I would now be able to teach my young pupils to read. The illustrations of Peter and Jane (and Pat the dog) showed an idyllic England of the 1950s, so unlike anything my pupils would have experienced. I had a spare suitcase and filled it up. It weighed a ton and would probably take up most of our luggage allowance. Since, on our return to Saudi, we were heading for hot weather, I didn't need to take heavy clothing so the allowance could all be taken up with books. I just hoped that the security officials at Riyadh airport wouldn't see fit to impound them.

One day on a trip into the town centre, I asked Anna if she wanted to have her ears pierced.

'Yes,' she replied with enthusiasm. 'I can wear my little gold flowers.' I had brought them back from Saudi ready for use. It was a wet day and she had spotted in a toy shop a bright red child's umbrella which, although not a Hello Kitty umbrella, was eminently desirable. 'Well, I'll think about it later,' I assured her. She sat in a comfy chair in the earring shop ready for the hole-punching operation. The poor child had no idea what was coming and promptly screamed like a stuck pig when the first hole had been made. She looked at me in the mirror through tears that were pouring down her face. 'You didn't say!' she shouted at me. 'It hurt!'

'Yes, darling, but it will soon be better. Look, Mummy has earrings and you'll find they'll soon be better.' It then dawned on her that there was another hole to be made.

'No, Mummy! Please no!' She scrambled out of the chair ready to run out of the shop. I caught her and sat her on my lap trying to coax her into having the other ear done. 'You can't go around with only one earring,' I reasoned.

'Don't care,' she sobbed. Eventually, she calmed down and I mentioned the red umbrella.

There was silence then she said, 'Can I have it now?'

'Yes, just as soon as we leave the shop and you have both ears done.' She sniffed and hickupped and weighed up the pros and cons. I felt like Judas in my betrayal of her trust and wished I hadn't started on the whole business in the first place. However, in a second, the hole could be made and we would be off to the toy shop. I nodded to the assistant who fired the bolt through the other earlobe and the job was done, bar the screaming. A pair of gold 'sleepers' were put through the holes whilst they were healing and the gold flowers could go in shortly after. The red umbrella was promptly purchased and put to use. Feeling the need to atone for my cruel behaviour, Anna had the pick of several other desirable toys as some sort of recompense.

Jake spent a couple of days at his old school, just to meet up with his old classmates and see his teachers. On the whole, I think he preferred his new life. Living in a sunny climate makes everything more exciting. He was seeing England at a particularly dismal time of year and he had yet to experience the searing heat of a Saudi summer. His school in Riyadh was well run and could offer swimming and gymnastics as well as football. Out-of-school activities were more problematic since we couldn't let him out of sight but whilst he was only young we could keep tabs on him relatively easily. I could understand why expats with older children sent them back to the UK to be educated.

Our mid-year break ended far too quickly. I packed a small selection of clothes and a few items that I couldn't buy in Saudi, such as nutmeg which was unobtainable. Apparently, nutmeg powder has intoxicating and hallucinogenic properties; nutmeg and alcohol were both *harram* (forbidden, as in *hareem* where men were forbidden except for the chap who owned the hareem).

My mother came to Heathrow with us to say goodbye. She held her grandchildren tightly as we stopped by the departure gate. It was so hard for her to see us go but it was to be harder still for her in the months to come.

Back in the Jug Agane

J UST AS NIGEL MOLESWORTH WENT BACK TO ST
Custard's with a heavy heart, so did I as we boarded
the Egyptair flight back to Cairo and thence to Saudi.
What inexplicably intractable nonsense was I going to
be presented with? The rule seemed to be, Expect the
Unexpected. At least I was prepared for things to go
wrong whereas previously I had thought Saudi Arabia was
basically something like England but with sun and sand.

My first intimation that I was back in the Mysterious
Orient was in the departures hall of Cairo airport. The
flight from Heathrow had been straightforward and the
disembarkation at Cairo only slightly weird. We marvelled
at the vast number of cats that prowled about the airport.
There were hundreds of cats everywhere. They were
obviously very At Home in this environment; some were

curled up asleep and others gazed at travellers without much interest. I supposed there was a plentiful supply of rodents around to keep them well fed. We queued for the toilets and I managed to stop Jake from going into the Gents just in time. Several men were looking at my blond son with more than a passing interest. As we entered the Ladies, an attendant gave us each a single piece of toilet paper. We all looked at our sheet of paper and then at each other. Previous experience in the use of toilets suggested that we were under-papered. 'More?' I asked the attendant. '*La*,' she replied. The Arabs have a very eloquent gesture which I used to her. You cup all four fingers and thumb together and hold up to the face of the person who is being difficult. It means, 'For Christ's sake be reasonable!' Reluctantly she gave us each another sheet of paper and we went in to face the horrors of standing toilets, which cause so much difficulty for women wearing trousers. Pulling trousers down without letting the bottoms of the trousers trail in whatever liquid is swilling around is a real art form. Doing it with a young child takes strength and stamina. Fortunately, Anna had a skirt on and Jake could pee in the normal way. A packet of tissues from my handbag was well used and much appreciated. I find you must always travel east of Suez with a packet of tissues to hand.

We had arrived in Cairo in the morning and our connecting flight to Saudi was during the afternoon so no overnight stay was required. We sat in the departure lounge for a very long time, Jake being absorbed in Super Mario again (what a hero!) and Anna colouring books and being read to. I chatted to a group of expats who were returning to the oilfields of the eastern region of Saudi Arabia. Some were living in remote tin sheds manning remote pumping stations only getting R 'n' R every two weeks in Dhahran. The pay was good but their lives were very hard. My life in Riyadh, even taking the Madrassa into account, was one of luxury in comparison. Our attention was taken by a huge hullabaloo that was making its way towards us. A crowd of excited women ululated at full volume as they escorted a bride through the departures hall. There was no mistaking what she was: she wore a vast white meringue of tulle and a long tulle veil and carried a bouquet of roses. She was glamorously made up and her flashing dark eyes expressed bridal happiness. I couldn't think what she was doing in the departures hall. Surely, she should be meeting her husband-to-be in arrivals? She sat down with her entourage and they chatted animatedly. When the call came through for us to head for the gate, she got up, waved to her friends and joined our queue. Another *cri de joie* filled the hall as she blushingly joined us. My God! Was she actually going to fly to Saudi Arabia in her wedding dress? She was and she did. Thank goodness her seat was several rows ahead and I didn't have to contend with the billowing tulle. Imagine the effect of a spilt cup of coffee! I went up to the toilet during the flight and saw how the passengers either side of her were smothered in wedding dress. Heaven only knows how she managed in the toilet. Somehow, The Dress arrived in Saudi intact and the bride was allowed off the flight ahead of the rest of us. Another crowd of friends and the bridegroom greeted her with more ululation and cheering. Brave woman.

We had another long wait for our internal flight. The airport lounge was spotlessly clean (in comparison with Cairo, or Heathrow, for that matter), so I made pillows from jumpers and laid the children on the floor to sleep until we were called. I watched the pilots walking through, wondering if I would see Anna's admirer again. I hoped we wouldn't have him piloting our next flight and the children would certainly not be visiting the cockpit. In the early hours we eventually arrived back in Riyadh. This time there was no trouble with our entry visas and we proceeded in an orderly manner. The suitcase of reading books got through customs without a hitch. The customs officer must have thought my children were voracious readers. The air was warm and balmy and smelt different to home, scented with flowers or spices and the dry air tingled our noses. Philip was waiting for us and, after hugs and kisses, we were quickly driven to our villa.

We had the weekend to reacclimatise ourselves before resuming the hurly-burly of work and family life. Once we had established when prayer time would be, we did a gargantuan shop at the supermarket, filling our huge American fridge and freezer to cater for some considerable time. Prayer time had moved forward in the two weeks I had been away so I had to recalibrate the best time to go shopping. Muslims pray five times per day and, in Saudi, prayer time governed every activity. Everything stopped for prayer, though I believe offices like Philip's pressed on regardless. Prayer time, or *salat,* moved forward eight minutes every day, so that it was very easy to get caught out. Not only did it move forward every day (because of the Earth's passage around the Sun), *salat* happened at different times within the Arabian Peninsula as the sun tracked its way over. Well, of course, it didn't move at all but it was easier to think of the Sun moving rather than us. So, you not only had to find out when prayer time was but find out when it was in Riyadh. If you got it wrong you could arrive at the supermarket just as the doors were closing and have to join the other irate shoppers outside. I soon mastered the art of squatting. It was particularly easy with high-heeled shoes, and I joined the other squatting shoppers. The best solution was to arrive just before *salat* so that you got locked in. You couldn't go through the checkout until the All Clear was given but you could get the bulk of your shopping done during the enforced closure. I never saw any of the mainly Pakistani staff praying. They just lolled around with their arms folded until they could open up their tills.

Prayer times were particularly annoying if you happened to be watching television. Not that there was much to watch on Saudi TV; they broadcast *all* the flights landing at Riyadh airport and *all* the departures. They gave great lists of eminent visitors to the capital that day and reported their adulatory remarks of how delighted they were to be there. But, if they did happen to broadcast a children's programme which coincided with *salat,* then the show stopped when *salat* started in Dhahran (doleful, plinky plonky Arab music for the duration) then the show restarted after *salat* until the Riyadh *salat* commenced (more plinky plonky music) then there was a further segment of the show until the Sun reached Jeddah. More music. It took nearly the whole time I was in Saudi for me to begin to accept the music preferred by the Arabs on the Arabian Peninsula. The notes seemed off-key and there were no discernible tunes. However, they were highly proficient clappers and drummers; intricate rhythms played out amongst groups of male participants at all-male gatherings. No wonder we desperately wanted a ready supply of videos. Fortunately, Jake and Anna were happy to watch the same films over and over and could recite their screenplays almost by heart.

I arrived at the Madrassa on the Saturday morning all ready for the new week, and all ready for the second half of the year. I had several suitcases of reading books, one suitcase being too heavy to lift. The children of my class helped by each carrying a bundle of books up to the classroom. The mistress-in-charge watched with interest but without comment. If she was pleased to see that I had returned she didn't say so. No doubt she would give the books a good examination after I left the school at midday. The children all started at base camp with the same introductory reader but the English speakers obviously made better progress. Even so, I was very impressed with the children who couldn't speak much English but who could nevertheless read, 'Here is Peter, here is Jane, here is Pat the dog.'

While I was waiting for Angelo after school, it was already noticeable that the heat had increased. Anna proudly produced her red umbrella and used it as a parasol. I had also brought one back with me so squashing into the lamppost's shadow was no longer necessary. Her earlobes had quickly healed from the hole-punching episode so we were able to take out the sleepers and put in the gold flowers, not without some anxiety on Anna's part, fearing more pain. However, the gold flowers did look very pretty and I was relieved that the holes hadn't become septic.

Philip came home one day with an invitation from Archie and Jenny to join them at a Scottish country dance picnic in the desert on the following Thursday, the first day of the weekend. How enterprising! 'We start with golf,' Philip informed me, 'then the country dancers trip the light fantastic with reels and strathspeys then we light a bonfire when it is dark and sing Scottish songs whilst we eat our picnic. Archie and Jenny will be bringing our food though we can add to it if the children want something in particular.' This sounded splendid though I was amazed that this could all take place in the desert.

'How do they play golf?' I puzzled.

'Apparently they take doormats with them to tee off and whack balls into the desert. I suppose they excavate holes at certain points. The "greens" are called "browns" and are already prepared from when they were there last time.'

'I bet they lose lots of balls. Where do they dance?'

'At the same place. They must have a flat area that is used every time. While some are dancing, others form a bonfire-constructors party and make a sizeable fire for when the picnic starts.' It is no wonder that the Scots colonised the world.

The good thing about not having any readymade public entertainment is that you are forced to invent events such as the Hash and the Scottish Country Dancing Group. They provided fun activities and also a framework where strangers could be mutually supportive.

We journeyed out of Riyadh in the direction that the hand-drawn map indicated and passed familiar landmarks which were always noted on our trips to the desert. 'I spy with my little eye, something beginning with PT [which for Anna's sake was pronounced 'p' 't'].' 'Palm tree,' was the immediate response. We rapidly went through the tried and tested WT (water tower), C (camel), W (wreck), sky and sand until someone noticed something unusual. M – mirage! These were not as common as you might think. Then there were DC (dead camel), BT (Bedouin tents) or BT (bath tub), though we only ever saw one of those.

The site for the Scottish party was, as usual, in the middle of nowhere but not too far from a rutted track and there was a clump of acacia trees and scrub bushes to give shelter. The sun was warm but it would get colder later when the sun went down, hence the provision of a bonfire which was already being assembled. Archie and Jenny had travelled in convoy and knew the site well from previous visits. We parked our cars away from the picnic site and went to watch the golfers. They were dotted around the landscape, gradually making their way back to the 'green', a dusty flat area which had the necessary hole with a flag standing proud from it. As the group assembled, someone brought out a large ghetto-blaster and slotted in a tape. The jolly music of Jimmy Shand and his band erupted from the speakers and the dancers quickly formed into the requisite groups to start their dance. It was surreal. There we were, in a desert in Arabia, with a large group of men and women, dressed in shorts, T-shirts and trainers clomping around in the sand. They were all concentrating on their steps and looked intently at the ground. When the dance stopped, they all laughed with relief that the weaving in and out of the patterns of the reel had gone well. Everyone clapped and reformed, ready for the next dance. Not knowing the steps, we opted to help with loading up the bonfire which was growing substantially. We scavenged for pieces of dead wood and any other combustible material until the fire-maker-in-chief declared that it was ready for ignition. There was no Guy going on top this time so we shouldn't have any complicated excuses to make. The last strathspey was announced and, as the sun was sinking fast, the fire was lit. It soon roared off and everyone stepped back from the sparks that were flying out. The dancers were now coloured red from the firelight and looked unearthly as they spun around.

In the background, at the far side of the dancers, I noticed that we had a visitor. A shepherd with his flock was staring at the spectacle before him. It was a bizarre event even for us, so what he made of it was anyone's guess. He had probably been attracted by the loud music and the fire, which could have been seen from some distance. It would have been a source of wonder that we 'advanced'

Westerners would want to spend our evening out in the desert dancing! As the dancers went to collect their food from their cars the shepherd and his flock drifted off into the night.

We all chose a good spot to settle down for the picnic and coolboxes were brought over from the parked cars and unloaded. The Bevan Feast emerged and we were encouraged to tuck in. There was a slight breeze, so the smoke was being wafted in one particular direction. Sensibly enough, everyone congregated on the side with their backs to the breeze so that the far side was empty and our side relatively full. The sky was black but we couldn't have seen the stars anyway since we were accustomed to the bright light from the fire. After a while, someone distributed song sheets and we all struck up with 'Ye Banks and Braes O' Bonnie Doon' followed by a succession of well-loved Scottish melodies. The fire had settled to a red-golden glow with odd flames leaping up as fresh wood was thrown on.

'Can I go to the car to fetch my Hello Kitty purse?' asked Anna. 'I want to show it to Jenny.'

The car was not far away and I could see it from where I was sitting. 'Yes, our car is just over there,' I said pointing to it. 'It's not locked.'

Off she went. Moments later she disappeared.

Gone with the wind

UNSEEN AND UNHEARD BY ANY OF US, A mountain of sand had been roaring towards us from the direction we all faced. The sand violently slammed into us sending the fire in all directions. There were flaming branches and red-hot embers whirling into us. The sand tore into our faces like points of needles and the wind screamed louder than the terrified people who scrambled to their feet grabbing children, husbands, wives and friends. Philip and I grabbed Jake and we both screamed 'Anna!' at each other. We doubled over to prevent ourselves being knocked over and struck out to where we thought the car should be. We couldn't see it. We couldn't see anything. After a few minutes stumbling and staggering around we found the car with the back door wide open but no Anna inside. We shoved Jake inside and shut the door before it could be wrenched off by the wind. Holding on to each other with a vice-like grip we moved away from the car in an attempt to find her. We couldn't go far otherwise we would have lost sight of our car. All the while we were bombarded by debris which hurtled towards us. 'Everything OK?' shouted Archie clinging onto his car door handle.

'No. We've lost Anna,' we screamed back. 'She's out there, somewhere.'

'You'll not find her with this storm raging. You can't see a bloody thing.' I was in a state of extreme panic and Philip was little better. All I could think of was the terror my child was suffering somewhere not far from me and how we were unable to do a thing about it. Archie bellowed the news through an inch of open car window. Jenny opened the window more and shouted something but her words were inaudible.

'Where's Jake?' We had to communicate by shouting into each other's ears.

'In our car, he'll be terrified by himself.'

'Look, Jenny and I will take him home. I'll go to the police and see if they can do a search of the area.'

Philip agreed. 'Yes,' he bellowed back, 'we'll stay here. We'll stay in the car until we can see something, anything.' Still warding off missiles that continually struck us we held onto each other and made the few yards to where our car was being rocked and buffeted. I slipped in as speedily as I could and calmed Jake who was shaking and crying. 'Archie and Jenny are going to take you home and Daddy and I are staying here until the storm dies down.'

'Why?!' He started shaking and crying again.

'Anna is out there somewhere and we must stay here until we find her.'

The poor child was now in a terrible state but we had to get him over to the other car as soon as possible. Jenny climbed over her seat into the back of the car so that she could hold Jake and comfort him. Their car was the last to leave and we watched their headlights bouncing up and down as they took the track back to the main road.

In the back of our car we shook and cried and clung to each other in mutual misery. The car was constantly being hit. At every blow we cowered and ducked expecting a window to be blown in. There was an almighty crash at one point when I think we must have been hit by an oil drum. We could see a sizeable dint in the car when we were finally able to get out without being blown away. Neither of us slept, being too distraught from wild thoughts and the maelstrom that assaulted us. My mind constantly pictured my sweet pretty girl cowering from all that assailed her. Sometimes I cried from thinking and sometimes I just howled from impotent grief. Philip let out a stream of expletives which expressed his rage at not being able to search for her.

Eventually, we could feel that the storm was abating; the car shook less and the noise lessened so that we could talk to each other. The sky lightened to a murky brown although visibility was still limited. I had a decorative neckscarf which I was able to tie over my nose and mouth but Philip had to manage with a large handkerchief. We stepped out into the waning sandstorm and began to search. He went in one direction and I in the other, though neither of us went out of sight of the car.

I looked around the area where the picnic had been in progress. The ground was blackened by the fire but the wood had been sent to kingdom come. Up in the acacia trees plastic bags and other flotsam and jetsam flapped in the wind but there was no sign of life anywhere. If she had been hit by debris or stung by a scorpion she would be lying somewhere. Not unless she had been swept up into the sky and deposited miles away. If the wind could fling an oil drum around, little Anna could easily have been deposited far from where she was lifted. I sank to my knees and howled again.

I heard a horn beeping in the distance and saw headlights coming along the track. I headed back to our car as did Philip from his search area. As we approached each other we exchanged looks of anguish.

Archie led a police car towards us and got out. 'No luck?'

We shook our heads. Two rotund, khaki-uniformed police officers got out of their car, as did Hani from Archie's car. Between us we explained to the police what had happened.

Their attitude was stunningly hostile. 'This party. You were drinking alcohol?'

'No!' three of us chorused. Archie did his best to describe the event as Hani translated. The police listened intently but with scepticism. They obviously spoke English but we didn't want them to get an erroneous picture of what had happened. 'You were dancing, mens and womens? Together?'

'Yes, but it is quite normal in... England,' Archie insisted. He wasn't going to confuse the issue by quibbling about the different parts of the UK.

'Our Queen enjoys country dancing!' I added somewhat superfluously.

Philip interjected, 'It was an innocent family gathering. Some of us played golf, some of us did country dancing and some of us built a fire. We all ate our picnics and we sang a few songs. That's all.'

'How you play golf?' The concept of playing golf in the desert had obviously never occurred to them.

We were losing precious time. 'Oh, bugger the golf!' I cried, pointing towards the swirling brown fog. 'My daughter is out there. We must find her!' I rushed to the car, found my handbag and pulled out a copy of her passport photograph. She looked utterly adorable and I shoved it under the officer's nose. Philip put a calming hand on my arm whilst Hani must have said I was under a great strain. Whatever Hani said, or perhaps it was after seeing the photograph, the officers softened their attitude. 'We will look,' they said. One of them tucked the photo into his wallet.

I suddenly noticed they were looking at my legs. I was still wearing shorts and a T-shirt and must have appeared almost naked to them. I raised my hands in irritation, shot back to the car and pulled out my long wraparound skirt. Once I was covered the men looked less affronted.

'I think the best direction to search,' said Philip, 'is over there,' pointing to an area of desert the other side of the track. 'The storm came from that direction,' we all swivelled round to face the other way, 'so she would have been blown in the direction the storm was travelling.' This made sense. Philip and I took the nearest sector whilst Hani and Archie drove off towards the centre-right and the police officers to the centre-left. After a further hour of scouring the landscape none of us had found anything. I then remembered the shepherd who had appeared whilst people were dancing. He and his flock must have been out in the storm. Perhaps if we could locate him, he might have some information. We all gave a description of the shepherd to the officers although the desert wasn't exactly thronging with life of any sort. He should be easy to spot if he was still in the vicinity.

'You two look knackered,' observed Archie. Without sleep or food and fast running out of water, we had to make a decision: to carry on looking or go back to Riyadh to take in fuel and get more help for the search. We also had Jake to comfort and make arrangements for. And then there was the Madrassa to deal with. Oh God, it was all too much.

Hani was talking to the police. I interrupted. 'Can you ask them what they will do about tracking down the shepherd and can they organise a helicopter search?' Hani translated my request and was told that they would look for the shepherd but a helicopter search would need to be authorised by someone higher in the police department.

'Perhaps we could call in there later?' I asked Philip.

'Yes,' he said, turning to the police, 'where will we find Police Headquarters?' They looked surprised that we were taking matters into our own hands and not too pleased. But the situation was too dire to stand back and politely let events progress at whatever speed they deemed appropriate. Being in a high state of anxiety, I wanted fast action and Anna to be found as soon as possible. Treading on a few corns was inevitable.

'Come on,' said Philip, 'we'll go back to Riyadh and come back here later.'

In the next few frantic hours, Archie contacted people from the previous night's party and members of the Hash to ask for help in the search. He took a copy of Anna's photo to be printed as a flier which we could put up on shop noticeboards and in windows. The more people who were looking for her, the better. I rang Sarah to ask her to find the mistress-in-charge at the Madrassa on the Saturday morning to tell her what had happened and to warn her that I wouldn't be coming in to school until we had found Anna. Jake was in an anxious state, wanting to be with us, but since Jenny was willing to take over his care, it was decided that he would go to school as normal, being taken by Archie in the mornings and collected by Angelo later. Archie would take a sheaf of fliers with him to the SAIS for distribution amongst staff, parents and drivers.

Philip and I drove down to Police Headquarters which wasn't far from the Madrassa, but because it was Friday, we weren't sure whether they would be open. However, they were, and we made ourselves known to the duty officer and explained why we were there. I was gratified to see an enlarged copy of Anna's photo pinned to a noticeboard. His English was difficult to understand but when I pointed to the photo and said, '*Binti mafquda* (My girl, lost),' he looked more sympathetic. He went off to inform his superior and we were ushered into his office.

The inspector was not particularly sympathetic and started the conversation with a grilling as to what we were all doing out in the desert. The alcohol, mixed-sex dancing, the skimpy clothing – the police officers had obviously mentioned my uncovered legs. It all sounded like an orgy. We strenuously denied having alcohol and tried to convey the innocence of Scottish country dancing. I said that if he could track down the shepherd who had appeared during the event he would corroborate our story.

'My wife is very sorry about wearing shorts and meant no offence to the police officers,' Philip explained. 'We were too distressed about our daughter.' The inspector nodded, somewhat mollified.

'Please, please,' I interrupted. That's as far as I got before I started sobbing again. Philip put his arm around me and continued, 'We are really anxious that the police should search the whole area as soon as possible. We don't know how long our daughter can last out there. Can you make a helicopter search? Perhaps the sandstorm lifted her and took her some distance from where the storm hit us.'

The inspector tapped his teeth with a pencil and considered our request. 'I will make enquiries,' he replied. We shook hands and left.

We left Riyadh with a good supply of food from the fridge and bottles of Nissah water. At the site of the party there were already several parked cars with people in the distance searching. Jenny was near her car with Jake who ran to us as we arrived. 'Archie has gone with others towards the south and other cars have headed east and west. I don't think anyone has tried the north since that is where the storm came from, but you never know.'

'OK,' Philip replied, 'we'll go north. Coming, Jake?' Not having a compass with us we took our bearings from the murky sun and slowly headed in the, thus far, unsearched area. Every hundred yards or so we stopped and looked around, Jake sometimes coming with me and sometimes with his father. There was plenty of stuff deposited here and there – old tyres, bits of truck, the odd oil barrel. My heart stopped when I saw a figure some distance off and ran towards it. But it was only a small dead sheep that had been detached from its flock. Already the flies were humming around it. I indicated to Philip that it was nothing to come over for. We travelled on some distance and I was beginning to worry that we might, ourselves, get lost.

'Bedouin tents!' cried Jake. We looked where he was pointing and, sure enough, there was a smudge of black in the distance, visible through the haze. We slowly drove over rocks and gullies until we reached the encampment. The residents stood and watched with interest as we approached. 'They won't like me being near the women,' said Philip. 'On the other hand, they won't like you pushing yourself forward. You walk in front with Jake and I'll be a few paces behind.'

I smiled at the men by the tent entrance, while the women had vanished inside. '*Salaam aleykum*,' we called.

'*Wa 'alleykum, as'salaam*,' they replied. '*Hinna, hinna*,' an elderly man said, pointing to a mat on the ground. They were inviting us to sit with them. This was a positive start.

I pulled out my photograph of Anna and said, '*Binti mafquda.*'

He repeated what I had said and looked aghast. '*Hinna?* (Here?)'

'*Aiwa, fi'l haboob lailat ams.* (Yes, in the sandstorm last night.)' We were rapidly running out of useful Arabic.

'*Binti hinna?*' I asked.

'*La!*' they all said, clicking their tongues and flicking their heads back, the Arab version of shaking the head.

I was staring hard at the enclosed part of the tent, trying to hear the women's voices. Trying to hear if Anna was calling. I wanted to go in to look but didn't dare offend them by asking. Was I going to lose Anna through misplaced politeness? The old man pointed to the tent flap. '*Shoof?* (Look?)' I leapt to my feet and entered the darkened inner tent where three women and a clutch of small children were sitting. We greeted each other and they indicated that I should sit. Once more I proffered Anna's photo saying, '*Binti mafquda, fi'l haboob lailat ams.*' They passed the photo to each other saying, '*Mumtaz, bint kwaisa.* (Beautiful, fine girl.)' One of the younger women said, 'We not see her.' I was surprised and relieved I could communicate with her.

'The sandstorm hit us last night and she disappeared. We can't find her.' As we spoke one of the little girls shyly came to take a closer look at me. In her hand was a Hello Kitty purse. My brain seemed to freeze. I gently took it from her and opened it. There, at the bottom of the purse, were two of Anna's hair slides. Each of the slides had been plaited with ribbon by the mother of Anna's friend at kindergarten.

'Where did you get this purse?!' I cried. 'This is my daughter's purse!' They all understood what I meant and looked alarmed. The younger woman said, 'My husband bring it to our daughter this morning. He find it in desert.'

'Where?!'

She veiled her face and stepped outside to where the men were sitting. I showed Philip the purse and she explained to the others. One of the younger men, whom I took to be her husband, told her he had found it whilst out searching for their missing goats.

'Can he take us there?' The three men climbed into the front of their Datsun pickup whilst we followed in our car. There was still enough daylight to see, but sunset wouldn't be far off. Archie and Jenny must have been wondering what had happened to us.

We bumped along in their wake heading west. Every so often we stopped to search the area but the desert remained void of life. Eventually we reached an escarpment with a few acacia trees and scrub bushes at its base.

'*Hinna*,' said the young man. '*Ma'fi bint*. (There is no girl.)' We all made another search but it seemed futile. As far as we could see she had vanished. With heavy hearts we shook hands with the Bedouin and said, '*Shukran*,' many times.

'*Wayn Riyadh*? (Where is Riyadh?)' Philip asked.

'Come,' we were told, so we followed them towards the setting sun until we reached a made-up road. They pointed in the direction that we should follow and waved us off.

'*Ana ashoof ya bint*! (I look for your girl!)' one cried, and they disappeared in a cloud of dust.

Hitting the buffers

ABOUT HALF A MILE ALONG THE ROAD THERE was a hamlet of half a dozen or so adobe houses festooned in electricity cables and television aerials. A few boys in grubby thobes skidded in the dust on their bicycles or kicked a ball. By the side of the road was a woebegone filling station with only one pump illuminated by a neon sign advertising Coke.

'We had better stop here to find out what is the name of this place. We shall need to tell the police that Anna has been nearby.'

We drew into the filling station watched by a tall, thin Saudi attendant seated on a plastic chair, legs crossed, arms folded. A cigarette dangled from his lips. Allah had obviously not yet willed that he should die in a petrol conflagration. He made no effort to get up to serve us so we got out of the car and walked over to him.

We made the usual greeting and I proffered my photo of Anna.

'*Binti mafquda, fi'l haboob lailat ams.*' He gave the photo a cursory glance and shook his head. '*Binti mafi hinna*?' I asked. He indicated that she wasn't or quite possibly, he couldn't care less. '*Hinna – shoo ism hathihi balada*? (What is the name of this place?)' Philip pressed.

'Al Rumaniya,' he replied.

'Probably translates as, "What the hell do you care?",' remarked Philip. 'Let's go over to those lads and see if they are any more helpful.'

The boys looked at the photo and all agreed that they hadn't seen her.

'*Shoo ism hathihi balada*?' Philip asked.

'Al Murabah,' they chorused. Well, that was interesting. Why had he given us the wrong name of the village? The attendant was closely watching our conversation with the boys. I hoped that the police would get more information from him than we had done. Either he knew something or had a strong dislike of infidels.

Jake was fast asleep on the back seat of the car so we drove back to Riyadh, once more leaving our other child somewhere out in the blackness.

The following morning, the first day of the working week, Philip took Jake to school and explained to the head what had happened. She readily agreed to distribute fliers of Anna's photo around staff, parents and the expat community. Meanwhile, Angelo took me to the police station where I passed on the information that we had gleaned from our search on the previous day. The inspector looked interested in what we had found and examined a large wall-mounted map of Riyadh and the surrounding desert. I retraced our journey home along the Dammam Road back to the turning which led to the village of Al Murabah. I estimated where we had joined the road and took a line east from it to the escarpment where Anna's purse had been found. I couldn't pinpoint where the Bedouin encampment was, but, being nomads, they were likely to move on to another location within a short period.

'The attendant at the filling station was very unhelpful,' I told the inspector. He shrugged his shoulders and said, 'Some people are.'

'He gave us the wrong name of the village. We got the right name from some boys playing with their bicycles. He said he hadn't seen Anna but...' I didn't finish my sentence, suddenly realising I was perilously close to making an anti-Saudi accusation. It was so frustrating that I couldn't tell him that I believed the petrol station attendant was keeping information from us. I wanted to bang my fists with pent-up fury but fear of ending up in a police cell stifled my dangerous thoughts.

'We shall speak to him,' he said calmly, aware that I was seriously overwrought.

'Thank you. Have you been able to organise a helicopter search?'

'It is in hand,' he replied. That could mean anything but he hadn't said no. I wanted to impress on him the urgency of the situation but felt haranguing him wouldn't help.

'Please telephone us if you have any news. You can also ring my husband's office if we are out.'

He nodded, stood and walked towards the office door indicating that I should leave.

Out in the car with Angelo I decided, reluctantly, that I would have to visit the Madrassa and explain the situation to the mistress-in-charge. 'To the Madrassa, please, Angelo.' He was surprised.

'Not to the desert, ma'am?' Angelo had been visibly distressed when we told him the news. He had become very attached to the children and cared for them as if they were his own.

'I have to tell them what happened and excuse myself from work for however long it takes to find Anna. They won't be very pleased with me.'

The mistress-in-charge was bustling her way across the playground when I appeared through the gate.

'Ah, Mrs Kate!' Her face was full of concern which completely undermined the brave face I had put on. 'Mrs Sarah told me this morning your little girl has been lost in the desert.'

As soon as I tried to speak, tears welled up and sobs jumbled what I was trying to say. Somehow, I described the picnic, the sandstorm, Anna vanishing and our, thus far, futile search for her. 'I am so sorry to let you down,' I snuffled, 'but my husband and I are moving heaven and earth to find out where she is.'

'We will pray to Allah that she is found. You come back then.' She gave me a sympathetic pat on the arm as I turned to the gate.

'*Shukran*,' I replied.

Angelo and I returned to the office to rendezvous with Philip and make a plan of action; Angelo was to collect Jake from school and take him to Jenny's office. She would look after him for the rest of the day. Archie and other members of the architectural team would go to the area where the purse had been found. Also, they would take fliers to Al Murabah to hand out to the residents. I would be surprised if the filling station attendant posted one up. Perhaps Mahmud, whose wedding I attended, would be able to extract more information from him. Philip and I would visit the British Embassy.

The embassy was in the Diplomatic Quarter to the west of Riyadh. All the embassies were within a short distance of each other, modern angular buildings nestling within a plantation of date palms. The Saudis kept all the embassies in the same area, the better to keep an eye on their activities. We saw a sign to the consulate so decided to start there. In fact, it was the right place to go since the consular officials dealt with problems that the UK citizens in Saudi encountered. After making ourselves known we were quickly ushered into the office of the consular duty officer. He had already heard on the grapevine that a child was missing so was expecting us. We quickly outlined the circumstances of Anna's disappearance and the searches that we knew about so far.

'You have informed the police?'

'Yes, but we don't know how much energy they are expending in finding her,' Philip said.

'We have asked for a helicopter search,' I added, 'but we don't know if anyone has actioned it or if it is possible.'

'Well, it would be possible, but the police are a fairly bureaucratic outfit and it would take time.'

'We haven't got time,' I insisted. 'Can you make representations to the Saudi government to try to speed up a decision?'

'We could, but they don't like interference. But we can ask diplomatically.' He smiled at his little joke.

'We have lost a child of three and a half years, three days ago. She has spent two nights alone in a freezing cold desert,' said Philip with some asperity. 'We would hope our diplomatic service would use every method possible to encourage the authorities to carry out a large-scale search for her. She's out there, somewhere!'

The duty officer noted our rising temper. We had to tip-toe around the Saudis but we were damned if we were going to be less than forceful with our own people.

'Yes, yes,' he assured us, 'we'll get on to it straight away.' He noted down all our contact numbers, including Archie's, and said he would update us of any developments.

We were heading out to the car park when we bumped into John and Becky McCartney. They had come to the consulate to organise an independent passport for Claire. Their faces were ashen when they heard that the missing child was Anna. They had already heard that a child had been lost in the desert but no more than that.

'Give us the location of the picnic and where the purse was found. We'll collect Claire from school and get out there straight away.' We gave them some fliers and after tearful hugs we sped off back to Al Murabah.

In daylight Al Murabah looked to be a miserable huddle of houses, all made from clay of the same colour as the surrounding desert. Despite the fabulous wealth that existed only a few miles down the road in Riyadh, little of it had permeated as far as this community. Either side of the road was a dusty area in front of the houses, which served as a place to park cars and pickups and for the children to play on their cycles. There were no children playing when we arrived – presumably they were at school. The children in Riyadh coolly wandered along the streets near our villa on their way to school with school bags confidently balanced on their heads. Here, in Al Murabah, the children must have been collected by bus; there were no school-sized buildings anywhere in the vicinity.

A flier handed out earlier by Archie was tucked under the windscreen wiper of a Datsun pickup. We banged on the metal gate of the house and waited interminably until there was the sound of someone unlocking the gate. The man who opened the gate looked surprised to see us, but not unfriendly. He wanted us to come in but we explained in our limited Arabic and with his limited English, that we were the parents of the girl in the photo and that we must '*shoof al bint* (look for the girl).' '*Inta shoof al bint*?' I asked.

'*Aiwa, Alhamdulillah.* (Yes, thanks be to Allah.)' The owners of the other houses likewise agreed to '*shoof al bint*'. Through the gates of some of the houses we could see in the background black-veiled women looking curiously at us with small children clinging on to their mothers' dresses. None ventured forth to take part in the discussions.

Finally, we made our way to the filling station. The same attendant was still there, this time tinkering with something under the bonnet of his pickup.

'*Marhaba*,' we called to him. He ducked out from under the propped-up lid and gave us a disdainful glance. He really had an unpleasant sneer. That, together with his hooded eyes, made me feel we were dealing with someone who was going to be totally obstructive. I held out a flier to remind him who we were but he scarcely looked at it let alone offer to take it from me.

'Photo in window?' I asked him, pointing to the window of his shack cum shop.

'Put,' he replied pointing to the plastic chair outside. I put it on the chair with a lump of concrete on top to stop it blowing away.

'*Binti mish hinna*? (Our girl not here?)'

'*La*.'

I left the two men by the pickup and wandered into the shop. There was a room at the back so I darted in to see if there was anything that would indicate Anna had been there. There was a bed, table, a couple of plastic chairs and a radio playing Arab music. As I was poking around the owner entered the room and angrily asked me what I was doing. At least that's what it sounded like. I held out my hands questioningly. '*Mafi hammam*? (No bathroom?)'

I understood the next bit, '*Imshi yallah*! (Get out!)' I shrugged and made my way past him, half expecting physical violence on the way. Outside I walked over to Philip who raised his eyebrows. '*Mafi hammam*,' I explained. I strolled back to the owner who was now propped against his door.

'*Hinna – shoo ism hathihi balada – Al Rumaniya?* (What is the name of this place – Al Rumaniya?)'

He didn't answer. 'Al Rumaniya?' I repeated. No answer. 'Al Murabah?' Silence. If I thought I could induce him into some sort of reaction I was mistaken.

'We'd better speak to the police about this,' I said to Philip loudly enough to be overheard. If he really couldn't understand English, he would recognise 'police' which is much the same in any language. Right on cue a police car drove onto the forecourt. The inspector I had seen earlier got out accompanied by the rotund officers who had come to the place where the sandstorm had struck us.

'*Salaam aleykum*, again,' I said.

'*Wa 'alleykum, as'salaam* once more,' he replied.

'This is the man who doesn't seem to know the name of where he lives,' added Philip, indicating the owner, who had decided to join in. 'We'll leave you to it. We are going off to search this area of the desert.' We waved as the men went into the shop. Philip got into the car whilst I peered into the interior of the pickup looking for anything that would catch my eye. There was just the usual jumble of rubbish lying around, though interestingly, none on the passenger seat. He had driven somebody recently.

'Come on, you'll get us into trouble,' hissed Philip through the car window, so I got in beside him.

'I'm sure he knows something,' I muttered.

As we bumped our way along the desert track Philip remarked, 'Just because he looks like an axe-murderer, he isn't necessarily involved in Anna's disappearance. Perhaps he has a strong dislike of Westerners descending on his country, swanning around in flashy American cars whilst he lives in a shack in the middle of nowhere.'

'Well, if I see him swanning around in a flashy American car, I shall know where he got his money from.'

'Where?'

'It's obvious! He found her and he's sold her on!'

'Don't be stupid. How could he have done that so quickly? Besides, he is still working at that filling station.'

'Yes – for now.'

'Well, don't mention your suspicions to the police. They would take your allegations of child trafficking as a massive attack on their country and the integrity of Saudis in general.'

As we approached the escarpment where the purse was found there were several cars parked by the trees. I recognised both Archie's and John's cars. People were conferring with each other and pointing in different directions. They paused as we got out of our car and joined them.

'No luck, I'm afraid,' said John. 'None of us have seen anything that might have belonged to Anna.'

A low thudding, thumping sound came from the north and we watched with enormous relief as a helicopter headed towards us.

'Thank God.'

'Hang on,' said Philip, 'it may not be part of the search.' But the aircraft circled around us and finally landed some distance away so that we wouldn't be pelted with sand.

Two tall, slim, handsome pilots walked over to us, removing their helmets but not their sunglasses. It was rumoured that only princes from the House of Saud were trained as pilots since they were less likely to organise a coup against the King. These two were urbane and spoke excellent English. '*Marhaba*, you are looking for the missing child?' one asked.

'*Marhaba*, yes,' replied Philip. 'I am the little girl's father, Philip Thomas and', turning to me, 'this is my wife, Kate Thomas. This is a photo of our daughter.' Philip passed them one of the remaining fliers. We needed more printing.

'Can you show us where the party took place? I believe you have spoken to Bedouins who have information?'

'Yes, one of the men found Anna's purse in this area here so it is possible she somehow got here from the picnic site. We were caught in a sandstorm on Thursday night so she might have been blown here by the wind.'

'Can you come with us to the place where she went missing?'

Philip turned to Archie. 'You'd be better at directing them. Can you go?'

'We can take two passengers,' said the other pilot.

As they walked off towards the helicopter, I called, 'Look out for the shepherd and the flock of sheep – or goats – that appeared during the dancing. He was in the same area when the storm hit us. I think the police want to talk to him as well.'

John added, 'Philip, you go home with Archie and we'll take Kate back with us.'

The helicopter blades thumped their way into the distance whilst we decided who would go in which direction. Mahmud and the others from the office took charge of the area towards another clump of distant greenery whilst we opted for the opposite direction.

'Mahmud, did you get any information from the people in Al Murabah?'

'No, no one had seen Anna.'

'What about the chap at the filling station? I thought he was particularly hostile towards us.'

'Some people are like that, but no, he had no information.'

'Thanks for asking,' I said, not hiding my disappointment. We were hitting one blank wall after another. 'See you back at the office.'

The McCartneys and I bumped our way across the barren waste. I had hitherto thought the desert was rather wonderful in its vast openness, but now I hated it. We all peered into the distance, looking and looking. From time to time we got out and searched around rocky outcrops or into gullies. I frantically stared at every bump and boulder, willing it to be my huddled child. She *must* be out there. *Why* couldn't we see her? My cries of despair at each thwarted search was affecting little Claire who began sobbing and clung to her mother. Despite not wanting to further upset the child I could do nothing to keep myself in check.

John urged, 'Try not to distress yourself further, Kate. The situation is bad but you'll soon be exhausted.' He put his arms around me which steadied me up. Becky looked stricken, reflecting the anguish she could see on my face.

Eventually, leaning against the side of the car, staring across a yellow-brown moonscape, we all sighed and I wiped away yet more tears.

'You know,' commented John, 'you are only as happy as your least happy child. Having a child makes you hostage to their fortune.'

As the sun set and quickly plunged beyond the horizon, we reluctantly made tracks for home. I had another unhappy child waiting for me there.

We collected Jake from Jenny's apartment and were dropped off at the AAC office to give everyone an update and ask for more fliers to be printed. Everyone was very sympathetic and wanted to help.

'What more can we do?' asked Hani. 'We have put the word out to everyone but so far...'

'Why has there been no mention of Anna on Saudi television or in the press?' I demanded.

'Perhaps they have not been told. Perhaps they have been told and are waiting for good news,' Hani suggested.

I thought this very odd. 'You are telling me that this story is not being covered until there is a successful outcome? Why wouldn't they want to mention it? The more coverage, the quicker someone will find her.'

'The authorities are very sensitive about bad news. They don't want people to draw the wrong conclusion.'

'Which is?'

'Well…' Even Hani wasn't prepared to say what that might be.

However, I was. 'I am beginning to think someone has got her.'

Again, Hani havered in his opinion. 'It is possible…'

'We'll see what the air search finds, but if she is lying dead or injured then surely someone would have spotted her by now?'

'Yes,' he agreed, 'you'd think so. Perhaps, *insha'allah*, we shall have good news tonight.'

Jake and I waited several hours until Philip finally came home. His face immediately showed that there was no good news. He sat down next to me on our sofa with Jake on his lap. Jake was really too big for lap-sitting but he sorely needed the comfort of his parents at that moment.

Philip recounted the events of the past few hours. They had flown to the picnic site and slowly circled it in a series of ever-larger circles. No visible sign of life. They then located the Bedouin encampment and landed to talk to them. The three men who had taken us to the escarpment where the purse was found again confirmed that they hadn't seen any child then or since. Yes, they knew of a shepherd with a flock who was in the area but they had no idea where he was now. Yes, they would keep on looking for her.

By helicopter, they then made a wide search of the area between the Bedouin camp and the escarpment. Again, they found nothing.

'However, the pilots decided to look around the areas we have already driven over and we eventually spotted the shepherd and his flock. We landed and went to talk to him. Both Archie and I recognised him, and the pilots translated for us. He said that during the sandstorm he and his sheep hunkered down in a huddle and stayed static until the wind had subsided. He had found Anna bewildered and lacerated, tucked in with his sheep as he moved off on Friday morning.'

At this I cried out in relief. 'She's not dead? Where is she? What has he done with her?'

Putting a calming hand on my arm, Philip continued, 'He guessed that she had been with the "dancing party" but said that he could find no one there.'

'But we *were* there!'

'He said he couldn't search for long because he couldn't leave his flock. He and his flock headed off in the direction of Al Murabah so that he could pass Anna on to someone who could deal with her.'

'So where is she now?!'

'Someone in a white Datsun pickup came past him so he flagged him down. The other chap said he would take her to the police station in Al Yarmuk.'

'Who was the man in the pickup? Was he the filling station attendant?'

'The shepherd didn't know who he was or where he came from. Everyone in Saudi seems to own a white

Datsun pickup so that's no help. He didn't take the registration number. In fact, I don't think he knew what we were talking about.'

I got up and paced about, almost beside myself with frustration. We now knew that Anna had survived the storm but had no idea who was holding her. 'Do the police know about finding the shepherd?'

'The pilots said they would report our conversation to Police HQ as soon as they got back to their base. We'll go to the police station first thing. I'll pop over to the Fillies' villa now and ask Angelo if he can take Jake to school and collect him later, just in case.'

Sleep was impossible for either of us. I was incoherent with desperation and rage, crying and thumping anything that came to hand. Only the fear of waking Jake stopped me from screaming. Philip was silent and drawn, staring ashen-faced at a blank wall. We wandered round the villa, occasionally coming up with suggestions of where she might be. My fraught imagination was now in full flight coming up with one horrific outcome after another. The thought of someone misusing my child for their own evil predation made me want to howl in despair. Philip held me tight and tried to calm me down.

'It looks bleak from where we are now but you've got to hold on to the hope that this will soon be a nightmare that we wake up from,' he urged.

I prayed fervently that whoever had her was treating her well.

Grey and gaunt we set off once more to Police HQ. Our inspector was busy with his staff but came out to tell us that they hoped to question the shepherd later and to try to get more information about whoever had taken Anna. No child had been handed over in any of the substations. He smiled encouragingly. 'We hope to have a good result soon.'

Since there was no point in going back out to the desert I decided to make another visit to the consulate to bring them up to date. Sitting around in the villa was driving me to distraction. The office said they would send Angelo to me as soon as he was back from the school run. Philip went in to try to catch up with some work.

Unfortunately, he was in the process of handing over the supervision of one project to one of his colleagues and taking on the supervision of a project for the National Guard.

The National Guard was an internal army tasked with maintaining order within the Kingdom and was mainly manned by Bedouin who had given their allegiance to the House of Saud and could be relied upon if there was intertribal conflict. A new city was being built to house the local members of the National Guard and their families, and Philip had found himself at a critical point in the project just as the disaster had struck our family.

The consulate duty officer was the same one we had met the day before. Dear God, was it only Sunday? It seemed like a lifetime since I had last been there. He was considerably more chipper when he heard the news that Anna had survived the storm and was pleased that their request to the authorities had been implemented so promptly.

Ever the distraught mother, I wanted to know what could be done to track down whoever had taken Anna.

'This really is a police matter from now on. We can pass on our concerns through the normal channels and thank them for initiating the air search. I think we can say that their prompt action progressed the matter considerably.' *Hmmm*, I thought, *it was a good job I had suggested it.*

'Have you ever had to deal with missing children who have not been found?'

'Um, well, I personally have no experience of that.' We were now on very thin ice and the duty officer looked more cautious.

'Since my arrival in Saudi six months ago,' I said, 'I have heard a number of rumours about Western children disappearing. I know of one child who was the subject of a potential abduction. My son was also in a situation where a young Saudi persistently wanted to take him off to "buy him presents". Little more than a month ago the pilot of a Saudia internal flight asked if he could *buy* Anna. I think we should consider the possibility that someone is either keeping her or intends selling her on.' By the end of my speech I realised my voice had become very insistent and forceful.

'Well, let's not get ahead of ourselves,' he reasoned. 'The police have acted decisively and we know far more than we did twenty-four hours ago. You must be going through hell, but try to stay calm.' I wanted to smack him but that was a result of my frustration rather than offence at his tone. He was right. I would just have to grit my teeth and try not to lash out.

'You're right,' I smiled. 'Thanks for your input on our behalf.'

'We're here to help,' he replied. 'Take our telephone number and then you can update us without having to come in person.' I took the hint.

Angelo was catching up on his sleep but quickly came to as I opened the car door.

'OK, Angelo, places to go, people to see.'

'Yes, ma'am. Where to?' The humdrum tasks of daily life needed attention. We were running out of food and clean clothes. 'I think we'd better go to Euro Marché and do a shop. When is prayer time?' Angelo consulted his Saudi-time watch.

'In a half hour.'

'Good, we'll get there before they close and I can shop until prayer time is over. Can you take me home with the shopping and then fetch Jake from school?'

I glanced at the Hello Kitty shop as we pulled up outside Euro Marché. Angelo and I sighed, both thinking of the time Anna had gone missing, only to be found there clutching a much-desired purse. I hoped I wouldn't bump into anyone I knew. I dreaded having to explain what had happened, but the first person I encountered was Nadia.

'Kate!' She came up and put her arms around me. At least she knew everything and I wouldn't have to retell the whole ghastly story. She looked at me closely with tears in her eyes. 'You look terrible!' she exclaimed.

'I am exhausted, angry, and beside myself with worry. None of which improve the appearance.'

'No, I can see that. The police are working hard to find her?'

'Yes, but...'

'You told Hani you think someone is holding her?'

'Whoever found her and took her off in his pickup has not handed her over to the police. We must assume he is keeping her or...' She understood the implication of what I was saying.

'Have you thought about going to the Governor of Riyadh's *majlis*?'

'No, what's that?'

'All the ministers and governors – they are all members of the Royal Family – hold a weekly *majlis*. Even the King holds one. They sit in a large hall and queues of people – anyone can go – line up to present him with requests and grievances they want sorting.'

'I will ask Mahmud more about it and ask if he thinks it would be advisable. Being a Saudi, he would know when the Governor's *majlis* happens – and where.' Having another plan of action to work on, I continued my shopping with more enthusiasm.

Back at the villa I had a list of tasks to perform. The one I dreaded the most was writing a letter to my mother and another to Philip's parents. I could have telephoned my mother but the conversation would rapidly turn into incoherent sobbing which would baffle and alarm her and be made all the worse without my presence to comfort her. Philip couldn't ring his parents for similar reasons and he was hoping every hour that good news would arrive.

The letters written, I addressed them for Angelo to take to AAC, to be included with the office mail for the Central Post Office.

Jake came in from school, starving as ever. 'Mum, it's my birthday this week.' I stared at him in horror. We had been so obsessed with our search for Anna that Jake's imminent birthday had never occurred to us. 'Yes, of course, darling. We must organise some sort of celebration. It won't be much of an event, I'm afraid.' The last thing I wanted to do at that moment was organise a party. Momentarily I felt a wave of anger that Jake should want a party but of course, he didn't know how serious were the consequences of her abduction and thought she was only temporarily missing. To a seven-year-old child, a coming birthday is a big deal. I did a rapid calculation and realised it would be the following Saturday, a school day. That was a relief; I wouldn't have to organise a party at our house. I couldn't face a houseful of highly excited children at that moment and, given the situation, it might have had to be cancelled at very short notice. 'It's next Saturday. I'll come with you to school tomorrow morning and ask Mr Woodford if you can have a party at mid-morning break. We can take in a good supply of snacks and a birthday cake for you to share out. Would you like that?' He was in full agreement. 'And we can go shopping on Thursday to buy you a present. What would you like?' He thought for a few moments and then said, 'A kite!'

'That's a good idea. We can go into the desert and you and Daddy can fly it.'

'We might find Anna.'

I sat him down and gently reminded him that she wasn't in the desert but was probably with someone. It was difficult to explain that although Anna had survived the sandstorm someone else was looking after her but we didn't know who.

His face crumpled and tears started to roll. 'The police are looking for her and interviewing people,' I assured him. 'We are hoping for good news soon.' I would have to ask Mr Woodford how Jake was coping with this turmoil whilst in school.

Angelo took us to the British School the next morning. The school was out in the middle of the desert miles from any habitation. It had previously been a commercial building but had been well adapted to its present use. There was a central tarmacadam playground surrounded by infant acacia trees and a continuous row of blue metal buildings on all four sides. My architect husband called them 'crinkly tin construction' which made them sound tacky but they served their purpose well. When I stuck my head around the door of Mr Woodford's classroom the temperature was pleasantly cool and the classroom bright and airy.

'Hello, I'm Mrs Thomas, Jake's mum,' I said. Jake's teacher jumped up from his desk and took my hand.

'Good morning. We are all devastated by the news of your daughter's disappearance.' We sat down on small classroom chairs whilst I brought him up to speed.

'How is Jake managing in school?' I wanted to know.

'Surprisingly well. His classmates all know the situation and are being sympathetic and caring. The school day is crammed with activity so he hasn't got time to dwell on the situation.'

'It's his birthday on Saturday. I wonder, if he came in with a supply of snacks and a cake, whether he could have a mini party at morning break? I really can't face holding a proper birthday party at the moment but we need to mark the day somehow.'

He readily agreed and assured me that all the staff were watching out for his welfare.

'If there is anything the school or staff can do to help, you've only to ask.'

'Just keep a close eye on Jake, if you would, and let me know if he becomes distressed,' I replied.

Back at AAC's office I sought out Mahmud. He was busy with Hani but said he could speak to me shortly. I wandered through the large open-plan office and smiled bleakly at the British expat staff who gave me friendly hugs. Philip was deep in conversation with various engineers but raised his eyebrows when he saw me. 'I am just having a quick word with Mahmud about the *majlis*,' I explained.

Mahmud came over and escorted me to his office. Hani waved through the glass partition; no doubt Nadia had told him of her suggestion.

'I believe one can approach the Governor of Riyadh at his *majlis* to ask for help?' I started.

Mahmud looked sceptical. 'It is unusual for a woman to attend a *majlis*, even more so a European woman. What would you want to ask him?'

'To do everything possible to find Anna.'

'He will answer the police are doing that. He might also wonder why you are at the *majlis* and not your husband.'

'I shall say that my request would be more memorable, coming from a woman, and that I am hoping his influence will reach further than that of the police.'

'Hmm. He might find that plausible. You will need an Arab speaker to go with you. His Highness will speak English but some of his staff may not.'

'Will you come with me?'

Mahmud looked at me steadily. 'I must think about your request. I will talk to my family and see what they say.'

I thanked him and left. I wasn't sure Mahmud wanted to be associated with where the search was leading.

Angelo had gone on a mission for Nadia so I had super-shot Efren to drive me out to collect Jake. I didn't really need to go but I was spinning my wheels somewhat with nothing to do except fret and worry. For a change, Efren was quite talkative. 'I am very sorry, ma'am, about your daughter. She is a very pretty girl. We all hope you soon find her.'

'It's more a case of the police finding the person who is holding her. Filipinos work in many houses and companies in Riyadh. Can you spread the word amongst your friends? Perhaps they might notice a European child in an Arab household.'

'Yes, ma'am, I'll do that.'

To fill up the afternoon I took Jake on an expedition down to Bat'ha by bus to look around the souk. The toy souk would be the place to start in view of Jake's impending birthday. I loaded a roll of fliers into my shoulder bag and we set off through our neighbourhood back streets to Airport Street where the bus stopped. The buses were single-deckers and strictly segregated. The front three-quarters of the bus was for male passengers and women had to sit at the back – rather like black people in previous times were forced to do in the American Deep South. We even had our own exit so that we didn't have to come in contact with men. I was partly amused and partly irritated. Throughout the afternoon I stared hard at every small girl I saw through my dark sunglasses. However futile, there was always hope.

We saw a number of different kites for sale in the toy souk and made a mental note of where we would find them on Thursday when we came with Philip. 'Can I have a skateboard as well?' Jake's attention had been caught by a display of brightly coloured boards with equally lurid wheels.

'Do you think you could ride one?'

'Yes! Of course!'

'Well, I'll get you one now.' It was lovely to have one happy child.

The women's souk was open so we went in to investigate. It didn't open on a regular basis but it was worth a visit. I had heard it was possible to buy freshwater pearls from the Arabian Gulf from there and I hadn't seen any for sale elsewhere. Jake didn't yet count as a man so was able to come into the souk with me. The vendors were Arab women, many of them black, sitting on the ground under canvas awnings to shelter them from the sun. They mainly sold jewellery and trinkets. I was always surprised to see black Arabs; perhaps they were the descendants of slaves brought by Arab slavers. I was shocked to be told that slavery in Arabia wasn't banned until the 1960s. To each of the stallholders I showed them a flier and said, '*Binti mafquda ar'Riyadh. Binti hinna*? (My daughter is lost in Riyadh. My daughter is here?)' This phrase tripped off my tongue so fluently, having said it so often, people thought my Arabic was better than it actually was so they told me lots of things which I didn't understand. I made a telephone sign with my hand and pointed to the number saying, '*Shoof*?'

One of the stalls had strings of pretty little pearls reminiscent of Rice Crispies. The seller didn't speak English but through a sign language of holding up different groupings of fingers, we struck a bargain and I bought five strings. I figured I would have enough to make one presentable necklace of lu'lu, the charming name for pearls in Arabic.

The freshwater pearls came from an amazing source. The Arabian Peninsula is on a tectonic plate of its own, slightly tilted so that the rainwater that falls on the Asir mountains in the west slowly filters through the lower rock strata for 10,000 years, eventually appearing on the east coast of Arabia. The Arabs of that region had discovered aeons ago that fresh water, always a precious commodity in desert lands, was percolating into the sea. They captured it by swimming down to the source with empty camel-skin bags and filling them up, bringing the fresh drinkable water up with them. This is where the lu'lu came from. I looked at my pearls with amazement. Having distributed my roll of fliers, we wended our way back through the souks hoping to see Anna at any moment.

The sun was going down so we had to make haste before darkness descended. I wondered what Tuesday would bring.

The Majlis

PHILIP HAD TAKEN JAKE TO SCHOOL WHILST I sat and stared at nothing in particular, drumming my fingers on the dining room table. We had a rather fine painting of camels and their riders charging heroically across the desert which gradually came into focus as I stared ahead. We had inherited the painting from the previous tenants of the house. It wasn't one that Philip and I would ordinarily have chosen, but over the months of living with it I began to appreciate its qualities. It certainly captured the ferocious tenacity and fearlessness of those who lived in that barren, unyielding terrain. They were a proud disdainful people who had never been conquered; why would any of the Great Powers want to conquer them? There was nothing there. Nothing until the Americans found a use for the black gold which oozed out of the ground. Being astute as well as wily, the Arabs, under the leadership of Abdulaziz Al Saud, had taken the oil production into their own hands and made the House of Saud, as well as many of their countrymen, wealthy beyond the dreams of Croesus.

The man who I wanted to intercede on my behalf was the Governor of Riyadh, a descendant of the founder of Saudi Arabia. He had a reputation for not suffering fools gladly but was even-handed in his judgements. Obviously, a man to be reckoned with.

The telephone rang. I braced myself before lifting the receiver, hoping it wouldn't be bad news.

'*Marhaba*, it's Mahmud here.'

'*Marhaba*. How are you?'

'Fine, thanks. I think you should go to the Governor's *majlis*. As you say, nothing ventured, nothing gained.'

'And you'll come with me?'

'Yes, but Philip should be there also.'

'Thank you very much, Mahmud. We are very grateful.'

'Can you come to the office this morning and we'll decide what to put in your petition to the Governor? The three of us can meet mid-morning.'

Later, gathered around Mahmud's desk, Philip started. 'I think we should keep it simple. A brief outline on how Anna came to be missing and our belief that she is with someone in the Riyadh area.'

'Yes, but we have to start the petition in the correct way. He is a very important man and we need to address him in the appropriate manner.' Mahmud added, 'Also, you must be cautious in your speculation as to the motives of whoever is "looking after" her. His Highness will understand the possibilities without you spelling them out.'

Within half an hour we had the petition mapped out. Mahmud would translate it into Arabic and we would present the Governor with three sheets: the top one would be a photo of Anna, the second the petition in Arabic and finally the petition in English with our contact details.

'When is the *majlis*?' I asked.

'Tomorrow,' Mahmud replied.

I woke on Wednesday morning already feeling nervous. I dressed in a long-sleeved blouse and full-length wraparound skirt. I would take my abaya with me and a black veil-type headscarf. I had bought it when I bought my abaya but had never bothered to wear it. I practised draping it around my head so that it would show I was being deferential without it being unflattering, which many of the Arab women succeeded in doing. The days of worry and sleepless nights had had a detrimental effect on my appearance, so a modicum of make-up was required. I didn't want to look like a wanton hussy nor did I want my face to be streaked in mascara when the inevitable tears trickled down.

Philip came back from the school run having collected Mahmud *en route*. Jake would be collected by Angelo and delivered to Jenny who would take care of him until we returned. We had no idea how long the process would take. Thinking back to my first contact with the Madrassa, a good deal of waiting was likely.

Mahmud warned me, 'You may find that, being a woman, you are moved to the front of the queue, or made to stand to one side. Or maybe you will queue with everyone else.'

'Do you think there are toilets there?' I wondered.

Mahmud laughed. 'I have no idea! Better not drink too much water!'

The *majlis* started after midday prayers but there was already a queue forming outside the building. I put up my umbrella and shaded myself. I was already warm in my black outfit. Why, in this country of extreme heat, did the men dress in white and the women in black? Misogyny raised its ugly head in a myriad of ways. During prayer time the Muslims knelt down where they were in the queue, some having the foresight to bring a prayer mat with them. They all seemed to have an inbuilt compass and automatically knelt facing Mecca. Philip and I stood looking like fish out of water but we had no other option.

When *salat* was over, the large ornate doors of the building were thrown open and the queue shuffled forward. The petitioners were a motley bunch; I was the only woman and we were the only Europeans. Although the Saudis generally wore the same outfits, white thobes and red-and-white headdresses, there was a subtle difference between the wealthy and the less wealthy. The more affluent had whiter, better cut thobes and the headdresses were arranged more artistically, especially in the case of the young blades who arranged their headdresses in imaginative constructions.

Under Islam, men are forbidden to adorn themselves with jewellery but expensive watches indicate the status of the owner. The older men often wore light brown robes which were draped over their thobes. Some in the queue were Bedouins looking wiry and wary. One man in dusty boots looked as though he had just come off a building site. Another looked like a *Mutawa*, a member of the religious police, with his hennaed beard and nasty whippy stick in his hand. He eyed me suspiciously but found no fault in my appearance this time.

We were all kept in line by free-roving police guards who made sure that no one pushed into the line. Those who tried to do so were given short shrift and sent to the back of the queue. Once inside, out of the sun, the air conditioning cooled us down and we gazed around the large room where the *majlis* took place. The room was ornate and the colour scheme was predominantly red and gold. Around the perimeter of the room was a row of comfortable chairs on three sides, some already appropriated by elderly men. Dazzling chandeliers hung from the ceiling and yet more lamps were placed at strategic points on ornate tables between the chairs.

The Governor strode in and stood centrally in the room. He had aides to either side of him whose role was to take the petitions from His Highness and to put them into stacks for later perusal. There was a police officer, evidently of a high rank, who watched the shuffling queue with close attention. It hadn't been many years since King Faisal had been assassinated, albeit by a member of his family, so we were all watched carefully.

One of the aides spotted me in the queue and mentioned my presence to the Governor. He nodded and I, with Mahmud, followed by Philip, was escorted to the front.

I found I was trembling and gripped my hand holding the petition firmly with the other hand. The Governor looked at me steadily and then glanced down at my sheaf of papers which I passed to him. His expression softened when he saw Anna's photograph and then quickly read the top sheet printed in Arabic. He looked at me again and then at Philip and Mahmud before passing the petition to an aide and indicating that it should be passed on to the police officer. An aide pointed to the plush chairs and waved us on. And that was it!

'What do we do now?' I asked Mahmud.

'I think we wait in case someone wants to talk to us.'

The petitioners who had already handed in their papers, were sitting on the chairs around the room so we followed suit and waited. And waited. I could have done with Jake's Super Mario to while away the time. The high-ranking police officer studied our petition then left the *majlis* for a few minutes. About fifteen minutes after that *our* police inspector arrived and, noting our presence, consulted with his superior officer. We all waited until the last of the petitions had been presented, when the Governor sat at one of the perimeter chairs, stacked up the petitions on a side table and proceeded to work his way through them. The senior police officers who had been tasked to look at our petition took us aside and, in effect, asked why we were there.

'The disappearance of your missing child is being investigated by my colleague?'

'Yes,' I replied.

'Why have you brought this matter to the attention of the Governor?'

'We are hoping that, with his considerable influence, more avenues can be explored than could be investigated by the police,' explained Philip.

This was all too obtuse for the Chief of Police who turned to Mahmud for elucidation. A lengthy and somewhat acrimonious discussion followed in which I hoped Mahmud was insisting that time was of the essence and that the search should move forward expeditiously.

Turning to me he said, 'We have made an aerial search of the area where your daughter was lost; we have interviewed people who saw her or might have seen her. We have been working very hard on this matter.'

I tried to sound as conciliatory as possible. 'We are very grateful for the search that has been made – but still, she is out there, with someone. She is very young and will be very frightened.' The expected tears began to trickle down my face. 'Look at her,' I said pointing to her photograph. 'If she was *your* daughter you would raise heaven and earth to find her.'

'If she was my daughter, I would not have been so careless,' he replied.

Mahmud intervened. 'Mr and Mrs Thomas are totally reliant on you. They are not able to speak Arabic so cannot talk to people themselves. They do not have access to the media to bring the disappearance to the public at large.'

'We are desperate,' I added pathetically.

'Be assured, the police and His Highness will do everything to find your daughter.'

We thanked him and our inspector with tepid gratitude. We *were* grateful but wanted that extra something that would miraculously bring her back.

Walking back out into the glaring sunlight, I blinked away my tears and sighed. 'Do you think that has helped our cause?' I asked Mahmud.

'Only Allah knows,' he replied.

Philip

Anna's disappearance hit Philip very hard. Neither of us slept much and I would often find him, throughout the night, sitting on the edge of our bed with his head in his hands. I generally coaxed him back into bed and we comforted each other until one or other of us fell into a fitful sleep. Often a piece of innocent furniture would be thumped as a result of his pent-up rage. He not only felt the loss of his adored child but deep frustration that he had not been able to prevent her loss.

I had a tendency to lash out, loudly and virtually out of control. Philip became silent and withdrawn. Whenever I felt a wave of despair sweep over me, he would just lay a calming hand on my arm.

'How can you be so unemotionally involved?' I demanded.

'One of us has to keep themselves under control,' he replied. 'We can't both enjoy the luxury of ranting and hysteria.'

I opened my mouth then snapped it shut. I was about to rebuff his harsh accusation but recognised he had a point.

Looking grim and angry he said, 'I am the man in this family. It is my job to protect you all and to keep you from harm. I have failed miserably to keep us safe. I feel wretched when I think of Anna out there without us and unprotected.' He dropped his head and his shoulders shook as tears fell.

'*No one* could blame you, Philip. *I* don't blame you. We are bereft and suffering.'

We wrapped our arms around each other until the storm blew over.

Somehow, we had to keep the show on the road, if only for Jake's benefit. In fact, keeping up some kind of 'normality' helped us through the morass of misery.

On Thursday, only one week since Anna was savagely torn from us, we went on a family trip to the souk to buy Jake's birthday present. We scoured the various souks looking intently at all small girls. Jake was probably too excited by the prospect of acquiring his kite to notice his unusually silent parents. The kite was splendid with multicoloured streamers attached, and we promised the birthday boy that we would head into the desert the next day to fly it.

'Can we have *shawarmas* for tonight's supper?' Jake asked, spotting a *shawarma* shop on the way from the souk. This street food was the Arabian version of doner kebabs, which we had not encountered prior to living in the Middle East. We all found *shawarmas* delicious so saying 'yes' was no problem. In fact, we were so grateful to have him he probably could have asked for anything.

We called in at the supermarket on Airport Street on the way home for a few essentials, bumping into a woman whom I didn't recognise but Philip did.

'Catch you up in a minute,' he said before following the unknown woman down an aisle away from where we were heading. I was intensely curious. She looked Mediterranean, dressed conservatively but stylishly and had a preoccupied air about her. I was even more interested when I saw them both in deep conversation. I walked down a parallel aisle towards them and as I turned the corner saw Philip hand over a roll of bank notes. They quickly separated and went in different directions. Holding Jake firmly by the hand, I caught up with Philip and hissed, 'Who is she?!'

'Can't tell you now. I'll tell you when we get home.'

I was agog to find out. I looked sideways at Philip as we drove home. He looked normal – not guilty or pretending to be preoccupied with something. Surely, he wasn't *involved* with this woman? I felt cold and clammy and close to panic. I couldn't face another catastrophe. As soon as Jake was absorbed in one of his videos, Philip joined me in the dining room where I sat with my arms folded and my stony expression showed that I was ready for the worst.

Philip laid his hand on my arm and smiled with a certain amount of amusement. He knew me well enough to suspect where my imagination had led me.

'She's Livia Manchetti and is married to an Italian architect called Gian-Carlo. He used to call into the office from time to time and occasionally Livia came with him. Gian-Carlo is now under house arrest because his boss, a Palestinian, bolted from Saudi with a very large suitcase of cash – you remember I mentioned it? The police have impounded his and Livia's passports and refuse to let them leave the Kingdom until the cash is returned!'

'Even though he wasn't responsible!' I asked, astounded. 'What are they living on?'

'Handouts from the expat community. I gave her some money in the supermarket. She and Gian-Carlo are not doing at all well, poor things. God knows how the situation will be resolved.' I was filled with relief and was ready to show the Italian Lovely vast amounts of sympathy. My mental image of Livia rapidly morphed from a Latin Siren into a Diva of Despair. Although her situation could not be compared to mine, it was pretty bloody awful.

'This country has the capacity to wreck lives,' I concluded.

The birthday expedition started early with food packed into a coolbox and drinks in another. With victuals and kite safely stowed in the boot, we drove first to Ghat Ghat, the red hills of sand dunes where the children had sledged a few months before. Everywhere we revisited brought back bittersweet memories. It seemed so wrong that we should be out in the desert ostensibly 'having fun' whilst only a few miles away Anna was being held in God knows what circumstances. But what was the alternative? Who knew where we would stumble across her? In the souk, in the desert, in some out-of-the-way filling station? The frustration of not being able to do anything constructive was wearing us down. Fortunately, Jake was so delighted with his new toy that we shook off our despondency and enjoyed flinging the kite up in the air and seeing the warm air currents lift it with the streamers trailing behind.

The colours of the landscape were powerfully dramatic. The sky was an intense blue competing with the vibrant hues of the red sand dunes rising in undulating peaks and waves towards the horizon. The contrast of colours between the kite and the sky lifted the spirits and gave us some respite from our normal thoughts.

After the kite had had a good airing, we pressed on to Graffiti Rock, a few miles further down the road. The red sand dunes had given way to the normal ochred moonscape. However, a large outcrop of rock reared up out of the relatively flat desert, our next port of call. Several other cars were parked around it and the rock was being scrambled over by adventuresome children.

Graffiti Rock was so called because large areas had been decorated with stylised drawings of animals, palm trees and humans. It was thought that some graffiti had been inscribed in Neolithic times and certainly many dated from when the geography of the area had been very different. The petroglyphs on the north face depicted hundreds of figures including camels and ostriches and even a battle scene. Those on the eastern face were much older, showing extinct aurochs suggesting that, formerly, there was sufficient vegetation to sustain a variety of animals other than camels.

Although it was a marvellous place for the children to clamber about, you had to worry about the preservation of the site. It would be just as reprehensible to organise rock climbing on Stonehenge or cave exploration in Lascaux. Hopefully, the Saudis would take steps to protect this amazing site before present-day graffiti scrawlers added their own inscriptions.

We met several people whom we knew from the Hash. They cautiously approached us, not wanting to intrude on our privacy but needing to assure us of their heartfelt good wishes. We briefly explained the current situation and handed out yet more fliers for them to distribute.

'Mrs Kate! Mrs Kate!' called a child's voice. It was Amal, one of my pupils from the Madrassa. We greeted each other warmly and her parents joined us, also with some uncertainty.

'Mrs Kate,' said Amal's Egyptian mother, 'we are so very sorry about your little girl.' She hadn't picked up an Irish accent whilst living in Cork as her children had. Yet again, we explained what had happened and offloaded more fliers for distribution.

'Mrs Kate, when are you coming back to school?'

'Shhhhh, Amal!' remonstrated her mother. Turning to me, 'She misses you very much as do all of the children. But we understand why you must stay away.'

'Well, I told the mistress-in-charge that I would not come back until we have found Anna, but now we know she is being held by someone, there is little we can do until the police find her.'

'It is so shocking. We cannot understand how someone could be so cruel. We are praying that Allah will be good.'

Philip and I thanked them for their prayers and good wishes and moved on to find Jake, who had clambered up the rock with Amal and her brother.

On the journey home I said, 'Perhaps I should go back to the Madrassa. Sitting around in the villa will drive me nuts.'

'Well, if you feel you are able to cope, then perhaps you should. It will be a distraction, if nothing else.'

Returning from taking Jake and his birthday cake and party snacks to school, Angelo took me to the Madrassa where I sought out my boss. She was taking morning line-up with the children, which involved a short talk in Arabic and the children doing exercises whilst singing a tuneful ditty in which the numbers one to ten were sung in Arabic – *Wahed, Ithneen, Talatha, Arba'a* and so on. I had learned my numbers thoroughly from the daily repetition by the children.

She spotted me as I entered the front yard and gave me a welcoming smile.

'Look, children! Mrs Kate has come to visit us!'

My class cheered and even the other children who had little contact with me looked pleased.

'Have you come back?' they wanted to know.

'Perhaps, soon. I must talk to…' and I looked at the mistress-in-charge. I suddenly realised that I had no idea what her name was. The rest of my sentence was lost in the hubbub of the dismissal from morning assembly so I decided I must remedy that embarrassment before I went to speak to her. Aisha was about to take her class away when I caught up with her. We exchanged a few words. 'This sounds stupid but I have no idea what our mistress-in-charge is called!' I said. She laughed. 'I can't tell you what I call her sometimes. She is Sayyida Samah. Sayyida means Mrs and Samah is her name – like Kate.'

'Thanks!'

She was waiting for me at the top of the steps by the entrance. 'Good morning, Mrs Kate. Good news, *insha'allah*?'

'No, I'm afraid not.' I took a deep breath and told her of our unsuccessful searches during the past week, of my visit to the Governor's *majlis* and the conclusion we had all come to that someone was holding Anna. I took out my well-used handkerchief, wiped my red-rimmed eyes and blew my nose.

She held her head in her hands and sat down heavily on a nearby chair. Her shocked expression was more eloquent than words.

'I cannot go out and find her, other than by walking around Riyadh in the hope that I see her. I cannot speak to people and ask if they have seen her. I cannot drive around Riyadh except with the help of a driver. My husband's company have been very good in lending me the office driver but I cannot have him all the time. So, what can I do?'

'The police are searching for her?'

I nodded.

'Then it is in the hands of Allah.'

'So, can I come back to the Madrassa? I shall go crazy sitting at home by myself.'

'Yes, of course. When?'

'Monday? If there are developments, I will let you know as soon as possible. Thank you, Sayyida Samah, you have been very understanding.'

The next morning, after Philip had left with Jake on the school run, I took myself via the back streets of Riyadh southwards towards the busiest parts of the city. It was yet another futile meander around populated areas where I might spot her. I called in at the police station on the off chance. The desk staff knew me well by now and gave me the usual regretful expression. Was this going to be my life from now on? The Madrassa in the morning and trailing around Riyadh in the afternoon? I would need Jake to be with me for protection. Single women walking the streets on their own were viewed with suspicion. A teacher at the British School had been taken into police custody on suspicion of soliciting; she had had a 'domestic' with her husband and had left her house in a temper to walk to a friend's house in the neighbourhood. Admittedly, it was dark and she was a glamorous lady but she didn't get far before the police picked her up. Her husband had to come to collect her, no doubt having to explain to the police why he had allowed his wife out at that time of night on her own. But I couldn't expect Jake to spend the weeks or maybe months ahead trailing around Riyadh with me.

As I walked, I conversed with the Almighty or Allah, as he was known locally; I had been taught to pray as a child but my religious convictions had lessened in recent years. Prayers I had learned always had an element of pleading: *Out of the depths, I cry unto Thee Oh Lord*, or *Forgive us our trespasses* or *Pray for us sinners now and at the hour of our death*. So, my prayers now fell into the category of asking for help, or more often, bargaining with Him. 'If You find Anna, I promise to help the poor/dedicate myself to good works/be nice.' However, the rational part of my mind recognised that given a world of suffering and hardship, why would the Almighty favour my prayers and ignore others? Then again, desperate times make us desperate for help, from whatever quarter. So, on the premise that 'if you don't ask, you don't get', I carried on my one-sided conversation with God. Besides, I knew my mother at home would be permanently on her knees and lighting enough candles to illuminate her local church. I had faith in her prayers if not my own.

While I resumed work at the Madrassa, Philip was deeply immersed in getting his new project off the ground, or to be more precise, into the ground. The National Guard city was to be built on virgin desert. The first stage of the construction was the removal of the top metres of sand to reach a solid surface on which to build. Meanwhile the contractors had to acquire water to build the city by means of the mind-boggling process of drilling deep into the desert, *through* the oil-bearing strata until they reached the ancient water that was taking its 10,000-year journey from the mountainous west to the eastern Gulf of Arabia. A water treatment plant had then to be constructed to make this water potable and also suitable for construction. To make the cement and, later, the concrete from which all the buildings were to be built, a nearby escarpment of limestone was quarried. The limestone was burned in an on site factory to create the cement with which the precast slabs of concrete could be formed on site, in the purpose-built precast concrete factory. The whole project was a perfect example of serendipity. The water was accessible, as was the limestone, as were the vast amounts of money to pay for it. All that was required was for the Korean workers to physically create this city and the European professionals to oversee their labours. AAC was employed by the National Guard and Philip was the senior consultant who answered to the Guard on the progress of the project.

Everything progressed well. The National Guard was happy, the contractors were happy and Hani was happy. Funds were flowing into the company and it promised to be a prestigious and lucrative enterprise. I was seeing less of Philip than I would have liked, since site visits could often involve an overnight stay, but at least it took his mind off our family catastrophe and his inability to do anything concrete to discover Anna's whereabouts.

This limbo of semi-detached life continued for several weeks. Somehow, we went through the daily routine of work, school, sleepless nights and, for me, perambulations around the city. If there had been tourists in Riyadh, I could have written the definitive tourist guide. As the weeks passed, the temperature increased and it became less possible to wander for long. Jake understood why we were doing it but found it very arduous. Whenever possible, he went to other children's homes for the afternoon or out to John and Becky's compound to play in their pool.

One evening Philip came in from work and came directly to me in the kitchen. He didn't say anything as he came in, so I looked up from making supper. His expression was anguished and he was unable to speak.

'Is she dead?' I cried.

'No, no. But I've got some very bad news.' As I gasped and put my hands to my face he said, 'It's nothing to do with Anna. I am going to be sent to prison.'

'WHAT?!'

'I think I'm going to prison.'

'What the hell for? What have you done?'

'I haven't actually done anything, but because I am the senior consultant, the shit presently hitting the fan is deemed to be my fault.'

Not for the first time recently, my mind froze over with blank incomprehension.

'Come into the dining room and I'll explain.' Philip put a comforting arm around my shoulders and led me into the adjoining room. 'On site we have a precast concrete factory turning out precast concrete panels which form the walls for our various buildings. Making these panels is a firm of subcontractors called Al Yamani. They are a well-known firm, capable of doing this kind of work.' Philip sighed as if he couldn't believe what he was about to say. 'We went to a meeting with the Guard today and they demanded to know why we were employing non-Saudi contractors in contravention of the contract which specified that only Saudi companies were to be used. The Guard says that Al Yamani are Yemeni – from the Yemen.'

'Well, that's not your fault!' I expostulated. 'You didn't hire them.'

'No, but as senior consultant I am expected to know pretty much everything and to make sure this sort of thing doesn't happen. The Guard said our failure not only contravened the contract but puts the security of the Guard in danger. The penalty for doing so is prison for those who made the error.'

I laid my folded arms on the table and placed my head upon them. 'Jesus Christ, this bloody country is destroying us,' I shouted in rage. 'As if we haven't got enough to contend with; our daughter is God knows where and you will be imprisoned for God knows how long. Aaargh!' My fists thumped down on the table.

'What's happened?' Jake came in from the sitting room, my shouting having drowned out his video.

'Mummy's cross because of something that happened at my work. I may have to go away on site for a while to sort out a problem. You'll have to be the man of the family whilst I'm away.'

Jake thought for a moment. 'Do I have to sleep with Mummy, then?'

'It's OK, old chap. She'll be fine in her bed and you can stay in yours.'

Jake's sweet response softened my anger and I took him into my arms. 'It's you and me together, darling. Hopefully, it won't be for long.' Later, when Jake was out of hearing, we talked over the situation at length.

'Who, exactly, has threatened you?' I wanted to know.

'One of the officials at the Guard.'

'Has anyone else been threatened?'

'The contractor's project manager, Luke Brackley, and possibly Jeff, our own site supervisor.'

'Hani?'

'Maybe. We don't know yet.'

I suddenly thought of Livia Manchetti from the supermarket. 'What's going to happen to me? Am I going to have to live on handouts from sympathetic expats?' I demanded.

Philip laughed. 'No, AAC will look after you. Archie and Jenny will be in close contact and keep an eye on you. Also, your passport is with the Madrassa so you can always plead exceptional circumstances if you need to leave. We have enough money in the house for you to buy air tickets.'

This reassurance made me feel worse. How could I abandon Anna and leave Philip in prison?

'When will they take you away?'

'It could be at any time. I just don't know. I suppose I had better pack a few things in case they come for me.' As he went off disconsolately to our bedroom a wave of despair crashed over me. The world was closing in, intent on crushing me with one blow after another.

The only good thing about Philip's arrest was that Jake didn't witness it. He had been concerned when we raided his and Anna's piggy banks for small change but delighted when we exchanged it for a 5-riyal note. Philip would need a sizeable quantity of halalas to use in the jail's payphones that were available to inmates. An expat of our acquaintance, the chief scientist of a water bottling company, had been taken to jail for turning right on a red light at an intersection. He had actually followed a police car around the corner but the police car had then stopped and taken the driver of the following car into custody! The irate expat was further annoyed to discover that he didn't have small enough change to operate the payphones. His Pakistani and Yemeni fellow prisoners were, however, very willing to swap a 5-halala coin for a riyal, making themselves a massive profit. The scientist was finally released when the city started running out of bottled water – the factory needed his presence to continue production.

I rang Sayyida Samah at the Madrassa, telling her that I wouldn't be able to come into school since there had been 'developments'. I would have to explain later. After dropping Jake at school, Philip and I went into the office to assess the situation and for me to get assurances from Hani that I was going to be paid Philip's salary whilst he was in jail and that Angelo would be available for the early and late school runs. Most importantly, we wanted to know what was being done to stop Philip going to prison in the first place.

Hani explained, 'We are contacting the National Guard and the contractors to remind them that Al Yamani's appointment had been made without Philip's involvement. We are speaking to Sheikh Mohammad [who owned AAC] to see if he can bring pressure to bear. I am sure your lovely husband will be safe.' His dark Arab eyes looked through his owlishly large rimmed glasses at me conveying sympathy and optimism. Behind him, through the glass-panelled wall, I could see *our* police inspector, with a couple of subordinates, enter the office.

'Oh God,' I said, as everyone turned to see the visitors. Hani went out to meet him. I held Philip's hand. 'Has he come about you or Anna?' I whispered.

The inspector smiled ironically at Philip and me. 'How do you say, out of the frying pan into the fire? You are not enjoying your time in Saudi Arabia.' Looking at Philip he continued, 'I am sorry but I am instructed by the National Guard to take you into custody.' Philip collected his overnight bag from his desk and returned to kiss my wet cheeks. 'Keep safe and keep our boy safe. I'm sure Hani will get me out very soon.' Hani patted him supportively on his back and walked down with him to the waiting police car. The staff in the office looked shocked and the Fillies also had wet eyes.

Then there were two

I T WAS A VERY TRYING TIME. I HAD SO MANY things worrying me that it was difficult to concentrate on one worry rather than another. In a way, my new concern for Philip's future stopped me from obsessing so much about Anna's plight. The more I thought about Philip's predicament the more convinced I felt that he wouldn't be in prison for long. The Guard had probably shot themselves in both feet by locking up both their chief representative for the project and the contractor's project manager. Rather like the diminishing supply of bottled water that brought about our acquaintance's release, the Guard would find that work on their city would grind to a halt without the two chief organisers of the programme. And surely, even in Saudi, people had the right to be tried in a court? At any trial, it was my belief that they wouldn't have a leg to stand on – particularly with two shot feet. But then, they did things differently in this benighted land.

Until Anna's disappearance, I had considered the Madrassa's idiosyncratic regime loopy enough to send me to distraction. Now, it was a diversion which kept me from dwelling incessantly on my other concerns. To be fair, Sayyida Samah cut me a lot of slack and I was pretty much left alone to organise my curriculum and teaching methods. She always smiled at me now and the other staff were as friendly as their lack of English would allow. Aisha invited Jake and me to her house for a curry, her husband being detailed to drive us back and forth.

Philip and Luke had found themselves sharing a large holding cell with a dozen or so other prisoners. He rang me as soon as he had been admitted and sounded calm and resolute which gave me courage to hope. Luke had not been warned about taking small change with him so was reliant on Philip's stash of coins. They were lucky to have each other's company and spent quite a lot of time discussing problems arising from the building of the city they were both engaged in. They should have charged the Guard for overtime! Their cell was basic and squalid. A dozen men holed up in a room with minimal washing facilities gave the atmosphere a rank odour which was compounded by the stench coming from the neighbouring latrines. Philip thought he would need delousing when he eventually got out. His cellmates were a cheerful bunch and highly delighted that they had British 'bigwigs' in with them. Ordinarily, their paths would never cross socially, so those Pakistanis who had a smattering of English enjoyed grilling Philip and Luke about their lives and families. Nevertheless, Philip kept a close eye on his bag and his supply of halalas. He didn't know how long they had to last so rang me briefly every few days.

'Hi, how are you doing?' asked Philip.

'How are *you* doing? Are they feeding you? What are you sleeping on? Have you had any news about getting out?'

I got the feeling that Philip was making light of his situation so as not to alarm me further. He said that the food was adequate, the bedding smelly, and Luke had been in contact with his bosses who were in daily negotiations with the Guard. He sounded positive, which gave me some comfort.

Despite being told that he didn't have to sleep with Mummy, I was glad to find Jake's body tucked up next to mine when I woke in the mornings. He went to sleep in his bed but migrated to mine at some point in the night. I suppose he subconsciously needed to check that I hadn't vanished like his father and sister.

The McCartneys kindly invited us to stay with them at the weekends. Without a car (or at least not being allowed to drive our car) we would have been housebound except for the bus that travelled down to Bat'ha. Since Friday was execution day I needed to keep us well away from the souks and Chop Square. John and Becky were good fun and did their best to keep our spirits up. Of course, Jake thought his father was on an extended site visit so we had to be careful about what we said. However, I knew I would have to tell him quite soon where his father was before one of his classmates did.

A new norm replaced the old one. Jake and I were at our respective schools throughout the mornings and I thought up a variety of places to visit in the afternoon. Apparently, there was a zoo but I couldn't bring myself to visit it. I had heard tales about the odd, misshapen animals housed there and I couldn't risk seeing animals imprisoned much as my poor husband was. I could take Jake to the swimming pool at the Marriott Hotel at the end of our street. Only men and children were allowed to swim in it but I didn't mind lounging in my long skirt and long-sleeved top whilst Jake palled up with other children and enjoyed leaping in and out of the water. As usual, I eyed all small girls in the unlikely event that her captor had risked taking Anna into a public place. There were very few places that you could take an energetic eight-year-old like Jake and I sometimes wondered what on earth the locals did with their youngsters. Playgrounds were well patronised by the children of Anna's age but there didn't seem to be much of interest for older ones. I took Jake to our local playpark but he was soon bored by the simple climbing frames and swings. He just hung upside down from a rung like a bat until I thought he would do himself an injury.

Archie came around to collect us for supper a couple of times a week but conversation was limited. The subjects I most wanted to talk about were off limits whilst Jake was listening. Every time I broached the subject of Philip's imprisonment with Jake, I balked at the thought of the effect that it would have on him. He was daily suffering the trauma of his sister's abduction, heaven only knew what effect his father's incarceration would have.

Then, two weeks into our new ordeal, Philip unexpectedly arrived at our villa. Hani came in with him just as Jake and I were settling down to watch a video. To say we were shocked, delighted and amazed would be an understatement.

'Daddy! You've been away for ages! I've got a new BAGA badge!' Jake shrieked. The BAGA badges were given for attaining various levels by the British Amateur Gymnastics Association which were taught at the British School. Jake was dead keen.

'That's great!' laughed his father. 'Glad to hear you've been busy!'

'Poo, Daddy, you smell very funny,' noted Jake as he pulled out of Philip's embrace.

'Yes, there wasn't much water where I've been. I shall have a shower just as soon as I've said hello to Mummy.'

I held Philip tight and kissed him in welcome. I looked at him and Hani questioningly as if to say, 'How has this happened?'

'Jake, you carry on with the video whilst I talk to Daddy and Hani,' I suggested, leaving him engrossed in 'Bicycle Boy', his name for *Breaking Away*, his favourite film. We went into the dining room and I was put in the picture. Hani had received a call from the Guard to say that the matter of the nationality of the subcontractor had been resolved and therefore Philip and Luke were now free to go home. Hani had collected both men, dropping Luke off at his house *en route* to ours.

'Well, how magnanimous of them,' I fumed. 'Just like that! They stuff you into prison on a whim and let you out on another. How arbitrary can you get?'

'Well, there was a lot of, how you say, wheeling and dealing to get Luke and Philip released,' explained Hani.

'But,' added Philip, 'it turns out that Al Yamani aren't Yemeni after all, they're Saudi!'

I knew then we would have to get out of the Kingdom as soon as was possible before any more disasters befell us. But… could I leave Anna there on her own? The mere thought of it made my blood turn cold. How could we abandon our precious child? But what would be the price of staying? Already Jake was showing signs of stress. His benighted parents were losing weight, looking hollow-eyed, ever watchful for the next crisis and living in terror that their daughter would be found dead. Whichever way we turned there appeared to be no satisfactory solution. Sometimes, problems don't have solutions just equally nasty options.

Philip went off to shower the prison residue from his body whilst I put all his clothes in a hot wash cycle. After Jake had kissed his father goodnight we settled down for a heart-to-heart talk, but before a few minutes passed Philip had nodded off. He was desperate for a good lengthy sleep so decisions, nasty or otherwise, would have to wait.

Limbo

OUR DISCUSSIONS REGARDING THE FUTURE tended to be brief, running on a well-worn track.

'I want to go home.'

'Without Anna?'

Sigh, from me. 'I don't know.'

'Why do you want to go?'

'I hate this place. I don't feel safe here. I am constantly waiting for the next catastrophe.'

'Perhaps we'll be fine from now on.'

'Perhaps we won't.' I wanted to say that bad things happen in threes, but Philip would have dismissed such a remark as superstitious claptrap. 'Anyway,' I added, 'I would have thought that time spent in a Saudi jail would have made you very nervous about the unpredictability of the people you work for and the substantial power they have to punish people who cross them.'

Evidently, his spell in clink had not reduced Philip to the same level of anxiety as I harboured. He would give me a reassuring hug and promise that 'things would sort themselves out'. I was grieving for my child but had no idea if the situation would ever have a conclusion. I occasionally caught myself in the mirror and was dismayed how gaunt I was looking. I had been slim and had a healthy appearance prior to Anna's disappearance but I could see the strain was gradually taking its toll. Having Philip back eased the situation but it wouldn't take much to unnerve me again. Philip buried himself in work and kept his demons at bay by concentrating on what he could control rather than what he couldn't.

And so, we carried on through this fog of guilt and grief, going through the motions of family life until yet more unwelcome news arrived.

I could see Philip had something difficult to tell me and was havering about how best to go about it. 'For the time being,' he started, 'the contractors would like a more continuous input from me.'

'Meaning what?' I asked.

'They would like me to be based on site to see the project through the initial stages.'

'You mean, you living near Dammam and Jake and me in Riyadh? Terrific. That's not much different for us than when you were in jail.'

'Except you will know that I am not in jail and I shall be able to come home for the weekends.'

I sat and stared at him with my arms folded. 'Do you really have to go?'

'The alternative is for me to go over several times a week, getting up at the crack of dawn and getting back late. Besides, you know what the Dammam Road is like.'

I did indeed. The Dammam Road was known to the expats as 'Death Alley'. It was a single-lane road in each direction, heavily used by huge trucks bringing vast quantities of everything from the docks at Dammam and Dhahran to Riyadh. Many of the trucks were beautifully decorated in a variety of designs with extraneous gadgets and mirrors attached. However, they were probably not mechanically sound and liable to break down. They drove dreadfully slowly forcing other drivers to dive past them before an oncoming truck appeared over the next rise in the road. The actual road was several metres above the surrounding desert so if you were forced off the carriageway you plunged down a precipice, ending nose down in the sand. Vertical trucks were a common sight as you progressed along the road although it was wise not to look at them for long.

'How long is this going to go on for?' I wanted to know.

'Maybe until the summer. But you'll be going back to England anyway in a couple of months. You won't want to be here after the end of term – it will be far too hot.'

'You'll be in Saudi through the summer?' I asked.

'I'll have three weeks' leave and can join you at home.'

'So, you want to come back and stay here for another year?'

This was a conversation that we had not yet entered into but Philip had evidently been giving it some thought.

'It would put our finances on a much sounder footing and, of course, I would be in the Kingdom if there was any news about Anna. I could keep in regular contact with the police and the embassy. You could get Jake into school in England for next September and come out here for the half-term break, Christmas and so on.'

I didn't say much for a while; there were too many ramifications working their way through my mind to either agree or disagree.

'Will Hani allow you to keep our villa?'

'I will ask him.'

'Would AAC still pay for our flights?'

'I will ask Hani. If not, you'll have to make your visits via Cairo. There's lots to see there, I believe!'

And so it came to pass. I had brought the children and myself out to Saudi Arabia so that we could all be together but we would be entering a phase when we would be torn asunder. I could think of no better arrangement, so finally agreed.

My final few months in Saudi passed in a routine of morning school for Jake and me and afternoons of various diversions to keep boredom at bay. If only I could have driven our car things would have been easier. I had been given a generous allocation of Angelo's time but I felt trapped in our villa. The temperature seemed to increase daily and trips down to the souk by bus became arduous. I was glad to know that I was not going to be in the country when the worst of the heat arrived.

Weekends were as active as we could make them; Jake loved having his dad around and sometimes we felt like our old family. Thursday trips to Hash walks and picnics resumed when the heat of the day subsided. I felt less enamoured of the desert now, knowing its unpredictable and dangerous changes of mood. Dear John and Becky generally invited us to their compound where we could relax and pretend that we were in a normal country.

My visits to the police station were never productive. Sometimes I had lengthy interviews with our inspector who said, basically, they had drawn a blank. Anna had disappeared into thin air. He could give me no encouragement that the situation would improve. After these visits I felt in a state of despair.

Easter was even more of a non-event than Christmas. The Madrassa carried on as usual but the British School broke up for a week. I could think of no alternative than to ask Sayyida Samah if Jake could come to the Madrassa with me for that week. She smiled and said, 'No problem,' and for a change, it wasn't. Jake was very curious to see my school and somewhat shocked at the paucity of school paraphernalia available to the pupils, not to mention the forbidding classroom with no artwork on display or interesting posters and very little reading matter. However, he got on well with the boys in my class and they enjoyed playing football with him out in the yard during breaktime. Being older, he was well ahead of the class academically and worked through books loaned to me from the British School. He also enjoyed helping my children with their schoolwork.

One day Sayyida Samah stopped me to ask if I would be renewing my contract for the next academic year. I was quite pleased to think they actually wanted me. What with my somewhat antagonistic attitude towards the ethos of the school and the time I had taken off from my teaching duties when Anna had disappeared, I had thought they would like to see the back of me. Not so. 'I'm afraid I shall not be renewing my contract,' I replied with regret, 'in fact I shall not be returning to Saudi after the summer break.'

'You will leave your child behind?' She had unerringly pressed the Buckle Knees and Start Weeping button. Through a blur of tears, I muttered something incomprehensible and went off to my classroom. I knew that when I finally got on the plane home I would leave my heart behind.

The British staff at the Madrassa still congregated outside Mr Sayyid's hut to swap intelligence, so much so that we called ourselves The Escape Committee. We could all see that freedom from the Madrassa and Saudi Arabia was within sight but as with all schools, the nearer the end of term came, the further away it seemed to be. Some would be coming back in September and others had worked out a way of getting jobs at the British School. The British School was wary of taking staff directly from the Madrassa in case they were accused of poaching staff, which in turn might have led the authorities to close down the school. Each company, be it a school, medical health centre or engineering consultants relied entirely on its Saudi sponsor for its viability. It was they who had the power to obtain entry and exit visas and were responsible to the authorities for how that company conducted itself. However, there was a pecking order of influence between each sponsor so if your sponsor happened to be a high-ranking minister or a wealthy potentate, your company could outflank another company by pulling rank. The Madrassa's sponsor must have been very influential because the British School was very nervous of upsetting them. Nevertheless, some Madrassa staff who were not reliant on the Madrassa for their housing and flights, such as myself, could work for a small expat-run nursery for a few months before applying for a much-desired teaching post at the British School.

The Escape Committee were circumspect about enquiring what were my plans for the future. They fully sympathised with my predicament and were heartily grateful that they didn't have to deal with it. I indicated that I was going to leave the Madrassa and become semi-detached from the Kingdom. AAC's previous inability to get me entry and exit visas seemed to have resolved itself, so I hoped that future visits would be hassle-free.

Most of the committee's concerns were with the end of term's exit visa – would it be produced on time? Would we get paid in time to buy flights or if the Madrassa was paying for them, could they be converted into cash so that people could organise their own journeys out of the Kingdom? One intrepid couple with young children bought themselves an 'all terrain, four-wheel drive' so that they could drive home to England. Not a journey that could be contemplated in later years when the whole of the Middle East turned into a dangerous and violent area.

A bonus would be paid to 'exemplary' staff, which I had no chance of getting. I considered myself lucky I still had a job after my recent erratic appearances. Most of us suspected that our less than compliant attitudes would count against an extra payment – but it was worth it not to be used as doormats.

As term drew to an end I applied to Sayyida Samah for exit visas for myself, Jake and Anna. If, by some miracle, she was found at the last minute, I wanted to be able to get her out. Philip also applied to AAC for an exit visa so that we could travel together; we planned to fly to Athens for a holiday, travelling by ferry to a couple of nearby Greek islands before flying on to London. But we were confounded yet again by Saudi incompetence and unpredictability.

The children's and my passports came through on time, each with exit visas. But Philip's passport, and several others from AAC, were lost somewhere in the labyrinthine corridors of the visa office. The visa official had, apparently, run off with a woman and taken the passports with him! Whoever would have thought that likely in Saudi? When the official was finally located, he said that the passports were actually propping up his desk because the legs were wobbling.

I had tidied up the villa, looking at every piece of furniture, every painting and every item of kitchenware, wondering if I would ever see them again. I buried my face in Anna's pillow and could still faintly smell her scent. A cascade of grief overwhelmed me. I sobbed and sobbed into her pillow, the pent-up misery pouring out. I ranted abuse at those who were inflicting such heartbreak on us. How could someone be so evil as to hold her away from her family? Eventually, I felt Philip sit down on the bed beside me. He rested his arm on my back and I could feel him shaking too. Glancing up, I saw tears flowing down his cheeks, his face crumpled in anguish. Gradually the torrent of rage subsided and we stared at each other in resigned apathy. This was a hell-hole and there was no way out.

I decided to leave Anna's clothes behind, just in case they were needed, and also her brand-new, unused passport should Philip, by some miracle, be able to bring her home to us. I packed all of Jake's and my clothes and items we valued, and stacked the suitcases ready for the journey. Then the fiasco of Philip's missing passport happened and I was faced with the prospect of hanging around our villa for heaven knows how long until the missing passport showed up. Keeping Jake cooped up in our villa for an indeterminate period was a grim prospect. Why couldn't things go smoothly for a change?

'Why don't you go ahead of me?' suggested Philip. 'You can book us into a hotel in central Athens and spend the time looking around the city until I can get out. It shouldn't be long.'

It seemed to be the only sensible thing to do so we rang the Athens Gate Hotel by the Plaka and booked a family-sized room. Philip cancelled his flight and we spent the last few hours in Saudi ensuring that the police and the embassy knew how to contact us should Anna be found. Archie and Jenny would be in Riyadh until Philip returned, so could stand in for us if need be.

By early June the temperature was always a consideration when venturing out of doors. We couldn't just go out and get into our car, it was almost too hot to touch. Ten minutes or so before departing Philip would start the car, turn the air conditioning on full power and leave the car to cool itself down before we could get in. Anyone could have driven it away but the alternative of getting into a burning hot car was impossible. Walking anywhere during the day was exhausting and to be avoided unless vitally necessary. The final days of waiting for Angelo after school were hard to endure; the sun beat down relentlessly and I could only stand it because of the shade provided by my umbrella.

So, the evening of my departure was one of conflicting emotions. I was glad to go but desperately sad. I steeled myself not to break down but armed myself with a bundle of tissues for mopping up the tears that were certain to fall. Philip drove us to the airport and saw us to the departure gate.

'Give me a call when you get to the hotel. I shall probably be with you in a day or so.'

I numbly nodded and kissed him goodbye. Jake hugged his dad whilst I gave Riyadh one last glance. I wished to God we had never come in the first place.

The Foundling

WHEN I WAS ABOUT THREE YEARS OLD, A mountainous desert sandstorm blew me away. Away from my family whom I have not seen since. Unlike Dorothy in The Wizard of Oz, I didn't arrive in a magical kingdom but found myself inexplicably placed in a Saudi family who were complete strangers to me. It has taken me a number of years to piece together what happened during those shocking weeks. At the time, I went through a deep trauma which took months, if not years to heal.

I belonged to a British family who had been working and living in Riyadh in Saudi Arabia. Our last family outing was an expedition into the desert where a crowd of us, adults and children, gathered together for an event; I can't remember why we were there but it was at night because our party was lit by a huge fire around which we all gathered.

One moment we were all together and the next I was on my own being flung around in a screaming wind that hurled sand and rocks and other flying stuff at me. I was thrown about, unable to stand still, bowled along the ground and then lifted up into the air before hitting the ground again. I had no idea what was happening to me. I screamed for my parents, but they were not able to hear me. All this I discovered later in life. At the time I had such a battering that I had no idea if I was still alive or not. At some point I found myself amongst warm soft creatures that had a strong animal smell. Even to this day, if I smell sheep, I feel distressed and confused. However, they gave me protection from the sandstorm that had engulfed the party.

Later, probably early the next morning, the animals began to move and I found myself standing alone except for a man who was looking after the sheep. After that, nothing made sense. We walked with the sheep until another man took me in a car to a house, and there I stayed for a very long time. It might have been hours or days. I was too distraught to know what was happening to me. At some point, I was moved to another house, the home of my new parents. As I was growing up I tried to piece together those chaotic events to make them coherent. Nobody could tell me how I had left my old family and become a member of another one. I always knew that I had had another family but could not understand what had happened to it. Looking back, my lack of Arabic only added to my confusion. Both my new parents could speak English and would have been able to communicate with me – but didn't. This is something they have never explained. They were childless and much in need of someone on whom to bestow their loving instincts. I was cursed by the fates to be taken from my first family but blessed by being given to another which wanted to cherish me. In hindsight, my parents' failure to search for my old family was very wrong but I could have been given to a less loving family or worse. I have heard that young girls, little more than children, are sometimes married to men old enough to be their grandfathers. Through my mother's and father's care I gradually adapted to my new life. I was young enough to quickly absorb a new language although I never lost the ability to understand English. It was deeply buried in my memory so, when I started to learn English at school, it came very easily to me. In fact, when other members of my family spoke English or I watched a cartoon film on the television, I could understand what they were saying. In this way I picked up things that I was not meant to hear.

The one thing that always brought back memories of my first life was my pair of flower earrings. Having them put into my ears, not long before I was lost to my first family, made a lifelong impression. I was so surprised by the unexpected pain I would never let anyone ever remove them in case the removal would be equally agonising. This event reminded me of my previous life – my mother and father and Jake; my brother was more adventurous than me so would always be available to blame when I was in trouble! I remember smashing a glass table by dropping a glass marble onto it. 'Jake did it!' I explained. But he was away from home at the time so I had to resort to the usual childish tactic of crying copiously.

Soon after I arrived, my new parents and I moved to Jeddah. My father and his brother ran an engineering consultancy and my father took over the Jeddah office. I can't help suspecting that my parents wanted me away from Riyadh. They were always very reticent about how they acquired me. The most I could get from them was that relatives had taken me in but there had been a death in the family so they stepped in to help. I had to rely on my cousin for an alternative story.

Unusually, our family was very small, just my mother and father and me. My mother had given birth to two sons, two years apart, but both had died from spinal muscular atrophy. Only in recent years has it been acknowledged that children born to close relatives often suffer genetic disabilities. Consanguinity or cousin marriage is very common in Arab countries, particularly in Saudi Arabia. My parents are first cousins and it is possible that their sons inherited recessive genes through both parents. Also, unusually, my father did not take another wife. He could have blamed my mother for not giving him healthy children but perhaps he did not want to add to her misery of losing the children and make her feel discarded as well. They were always affectionate towards each other, so my addition to the family must have been a comfort to them.

My childhood in Jeddah was very pleasant. New kindergarten schools were being opened in all cities, and mine in Jeddah was probably one of the most highly regarded. My parents not only approved of female education but could afford the best. Ummi could well have kept me at home since she did not have other children, but seemed determined that I would get the best of what was on offer. Jeddah is a much more relaxed city than Riyadh and where families enjoy living by the sea. We could never go sea bathing, of course, but we could take walks along the shore when the weather cooled in winter. The summer was hot and muggy so my mother and I would go to Switzerland to escape the heat. Sometimes my father would join us for a week or so. They rented an apartment by Lake Geneva where we and our maid settled in for the summer. Every year my parents enrolled me on an English language summer course to improve both my spoken and written English. This paid huge dividends later in my educational aspirations. My Aunt Salma often joined us with her three children to escape the suffocating furnace of a Riyadh summer. Their apartment was in the same block so we were always together.

This should have been a lot of fun but my cousin Amal took against me from the start. I cannot account for this; we only met on these summer breaks in Switzerland and on our visits to Riyadh or when they came to Jeddah. Our extended meetings in Montreux eventually became occasions to fill me with anxiety. I had become used to people saying nice things to me or giving me gifts in my old life and so it continued in the new one. I did not know this was unusual and assumed that all small children had similar experiences. All the visitors to the house commented on my appearance and my mother was always pleased to have a well-regarded child – even though she had not in any way contributed to my looks or abilities. Amal took my compliments with irritation. 'Ummi, I am pretty too?' she would ask Aunt Salma, who of course said that she was. Indeed, she was an attractive child but she resented people praising me.

As we grew older she began to insinuate that there was something wrong with me, though this was done whilst we were alone.

'You are not a proper Saudi. In fact, you are not even a proper member of our family,' she confided on one occasion. 'Ummi says Aunt Noura took pity on you because your other family didn't want you anymore.'

I had distant memories of my previous life so knew I had been adopted. But it was deeply upsetting to hear that my first family had abandoned me. I think I may have cried and she knew she had scored a direct hit. From then on, I was constantly made aware of my shortcomings. My mother brushed aside her remarks and said I was not to pay them any attention but, as she was reluctant to explain fully how I had been taken into the family, she never put my mind at rest. However, I overheard my mother and Aunt Salma having a heated conversation which suddenly stopped when I entered the room. My aunt left saying she would speak to Amal.

It was during our stay in Montreux that I first met my cousin Faisal. Of course, he was not my real cousin and not even a close one. I think we are officially second cousins on my father's side. There is so much marriage between cousins in my family, it is hard to work out our exact relationship.

Faisal is eight years older than me, so was a teenager when his summer stay coincided with mine. He and some other cousins were stopping over on their way to Verbier where they could enjoy cycling down the mountains. This sounded amazingly courageous and I regarded him with awe. So did Amal, who confided to me that she and Faisal were to marry one day.

'He is from my family and we are proper cousins. Our parents will want us to marry.' She wanted me to understand that I didn't rate as a candidate. I told her that I was determined to be a teacher and that she was welcome to him.

Aunt Salma and my mother decided to take a day trip by train to Verbier so that we could watch our cousins risking their limbs in this crazy sport. The prospect of going up the mountain in a cable car was thrilling and we all set off in high spirits.

Verbier is dedicated to sport in both winter and summer. In summer, the ski pistes become cycle runs for young men (I even saw girls riding on one occasion) hurtling down at breakneck speed on their mountain bikes. However, they have their bodies well protected by pads attached to every part that could be damaged. Helmets complete the outfit making them look like space warriors. Our party looked down at the starting position and we cheered each cousin as they careered off. We went to the café until they all came back up again on the cable car for their next turn.

As they assembled for the next run we watched fathers and children setting off together on scooters made for two. Faisal must have noticed how much I was taken with this activity and said, 'Hannah, would you like to go?' I was astounded and looked to my mother who was appalled. 'No, she can't!' she exclaimed. 'It is far too dangerous.'

Faisal cheerfully poo-pooed her objections, saying he would go down carefully. I would have a helmet on and would be totally safe. Aunt Salma joined in with her objections. This expedition was not going the way she had intended. Being a male, he was able to override the women's objections and before I knew it, I was helmeted and standing on the footplate between Faisal's arms as he took hold of the handlebars. I glanced at Amal who was looking at me with unconcealed fury. 'See you at the bottom,' called Faisal to Ummi and Aunt Salma. 'Look out for us from the cable car!' And off we went.

The ride down was one of the most exhilarating things that had ever happened to me. I had never been on a bicycle (my parents had never bought me one and our garden was not really big enough to cycle around) and the speed of our descent of the mountain was terrifying; my knuckles were as white as if I had developed rigor mortis. As soon as we arrived in the square below, I collected my wits and asked Faisal if we could do it again. He laughed and said that he was glad that I had enjoyed it. He bought us both ice creams to eat whilst we waited for the others to come down in the cable car and I suppose it was then that I fell in love with him. This was to be my secret, never to be shared with anyone, especially not with Amal.

A Grecian interlude

ATHENS WAS PLEASANTLY COOL AFTER Riyadh. Although the temperature was in the high eighties the sun didn't have the harsh intensity that we had become accustomed to. I looked forward to exploring the city with Jake and, hopefully, with Philip, in the coming week. As soon as we had settled into our room I dialled the phone number of our villa in Riyadh.

'Hi, sweetheart, we are in our hotel. Everything is fine here. No news of Anna, I suppose?'

'No, I'm afraid not. I called in at the police station this evening and they gave me the usual glum expression. They seem genuinely embarrassed that they have no idea where she is.'

'Have they found your passport yet?'

'Yes, it was propping up the visa official's desk along with several others. But you won't believe what's happened – the King's died. The airport has been shut down for the next week. Nobody can get in or out of the country.'

It was a good thing I was sitting on the bed otherwise I would have collapsed onto it.

'For God's sake!' I exclaimed. 'What do we do now?'

'Well, you will just have to stay in Athens until the airport reopens.'

'Why do they have to shut the airport just because the King has died?'

'You know how this place operates. Always expect the unexpected. I suppose there will be a period of uncertainty whilst all the top princes move up the pecking order. The Crown Prince will become the new King and I think Prince Abdullah, the Head of the National Guard, will become the new Crown Prince. And so it goes, down the line of the sons of Abdul Aziz.'

'OK, darling,' I sighed. 'We'll spend the time exploring Athens. I'll ring you every day at this time.'

The following week passed pleasantly. I could not stop myself from raking every street scene for small dark-haired girls and then peering intently at them. Rationally, it was not possible that she was in Athens but it had become automatic for me to look for her. Jake and I wandered around the Plaka, the old central marketplace that had existed in ancient times. It nestled under the Acropolis and we could see the Parthenon perched magnificently on top. It was great to wander around in shorts and a T-shirt without fear of being upbraided for indecency. I caught up with the news from home, free from the accustomed Saudi censorship of the British press. The Saudis had a department entirely dedicated to blacking out with felt pens any photographs they considered immodest. This included Princess Diana in a low-cut evening dress. I wondered what effect it had on the poor chap who had to spend hour after hour blacking over Princess Di's *décolleté*. As we sat drinking coffee and orange juice in shady cafés in the Plaka, the only news in which the British press was interested was the imminent birth of the next in line to the British throne. Princess Diana's first baby was due any day and the press were agog to see what she would produce.

We climbed the Acropolis and viewed the Parthenon. Thank goodness Lord Elgin had removed the marble frieze from around the top of the Parthenon to the safety of the British Museum. Apparently, in Elgin's time, the Turkish army had used the Parthenon for target practice. If Elgin hadn't removed the Marbles, not only would the Greeks not have them, nobody would. There were numerous ancient buildings and structures littered around the Plaka area. One marvelled that they had lasted so long. Every evening, Philip said there was still no news regarding Anna or the reopening of the airport so Jake and I would look at the map to see where we would explore the following day.

'Look, Mum!' exclaimed Jake. 'We're near the sea! Can we go to the seaside tomorrow?' I had noticed a car rental shop next to the hotel so first thing the following morning

I hired a car for the day and we drove down the coast to Voula. It was exciting being in charge of a car again and slightly terrifying engaging with the local traffic. It was not unlike the dodgems but without the bumps. I was pulled over by the police at one point but when the officer discovered I was English he gave up and waved me on. I had no idea what the problem was but it couldn't have been too serious.

I paddled in the sea and Jake swam in his underpants. We indulged in ice creams and enjoyed moussaka for lunch. I could feel the oppression of Saudi lifting.

A nice young man joined us and chatted for a while. 'Would you like a trip out in my boat?'

'Yes, Mum!' cried my young adventurer. After ensuring that our skipper had a life jacket for Jake, we scrambled into the boat and the young man waded through the surf to push us off the sand.

Throughout the afternoon I was expecting a request for an evening date or my phone number or some other suggestion that I would have to refuse, but none came, which made the whole enterprise even more pleasurable. When we had landed he bid us goodbye and we headed back to Athens. What a nice day out.

That evening, Philip had good news. The airport would reopen the following day and he would do his level best to be on a flight to Athens. After an early message to say All Systems were Go, Jake and I made our way by bus to the airport to meet the afternoon flight. He and I chatted away whilst waiting for Philip to appear. I suddenly felt a tap on my shoulder and turned to see a beaming middle-aged woman. In what I took to be a Texan accent, she said, 'I heard from your accents that you are British?' I smiled encouragingly at her. 'You have wonderful news! You have a new Crown Prince!' I wondered how on earth she knew we had come from Saudi. 'Er, um yes, Prince Abdullah.' She looked very puzzled and said, 'No, I think he's called William.' The penny dropped – ah yes, *that* Crown Prince! I thought I would clear up the misunderstanding with a nugget of information on Royal Family titles.

'Actually, the British Royal Family doesn't have crown princes,' I began. 'The heir to the throne is called the Prince of Wales; all other sons of the Monarch and the Prince of Wales are just common-or-garden princes.' She looked dubious. 'Crown princes belong to other royal houses such as Denmark and Saudi Arabia,' I added.

'Oh,' she replied but was obviously thinking, *Huh! What do you know? You thought Princess Diana's baby was called Abdullah.* Fortunately, our very own VIP appeared at that moment through arrivals.

'Daddy!' Jake ran over to greet him and I waited until Philip had disentangled himself from his excited son. 'Hi, sweetiepie.' We kissed and hugged, so pleased to be together and out of Saudi's clutches for the time being. 'What have you been up to?'

'We've been out in a boat at the seaside!' Jake told his father. This was obviously more momentous than any old ruins we had visited.

'Who with?' asked his father.

'Mummy was talking to a man at the seaside and he took us out.'

Philip laughed and said to me, 'Glad to see you're keeping your hand in!'

For the rest of our stay in Athens we visited the ruins again and ventured further afield in a hire car to the Peloponnese to visit Mycenae. The ancient ruined city had such an evocative atmosphere. We peered down from the highest point into the ravine through which the River Chaos ran. I marvelled at the ruts in the stone pavement under the Lion Gate, the ruts dating back to when King Agamemnon rode his chariot through it. One grey-haired woman was on her knees peering at the ruts. 'Look, darling!' she said to her husband. 'These are the very ruts made by Agamemnon's chariot!' Further up the slope was another English woman parked on a stone wall with her arms folded. 'Well', she opined, 'if you've seen one block of stone, you've seen the lot!' It takes all sorts. The short cruise to Mykonos and Delos were full of interest, good food and legal alcohol. Sitting on the open decks of the ferries, we turned from being tanned to dark brown. Jake's hair was bleached white blond and we felt fitter than we had for some time.

I had found that since leaving Saudi I was beginning to sleep better. My dreams were always on the same theme: Anna was lost and I couldn't find her. Sometimes she was missing in a supermarket and on other occasions out in the oasis in Dar'iyah. I often woke in a state of panic throughout the night. And then, in a moment, I'd remember that the nightmare was real and ongoing. Obviously, my amygdala and the emotion-related parts of my brain were trying to take the horror of recent events out of my memory and prevent me from going crackers.

It was good that we had this period in Greece between Saudi and home in England. We could shake the desert sands from our feet and prepare ourselves for the onslaught from parents and friends on our return.

Harsh words

I DECIDED TO VISIT MY MOTHER ON MY OWN. PHILIP could bear the brunt of explaining our behaviour to his parents and I needed to keep Jake away from my mother until I had calmed her down. She lived only half an hour from our house so I drove over on the same day that we landed. She was pottering around the kitchen when I arrived and had seen me pass the kitchen window. Nevertheless, she carried on with her tasks and ignored me.

'Hello, Mum,' I started cautiously.

'You've left her behind, then.'

'Yes.' Silence for a few minutes whilst she moved stuff around the kitchen. 'We had to. We had run out of all options.'

She rounded on me. 'You bitch! How could you be so cruel? How could you abandon a poor little child into the hands of those, those *savages*?!' She directed the full torrent of her rage at my selfish behaviour.

I tried to mollify her fury. 'We looked *everywhere* for her. The police are looking for her. As soon as she is found they will contact us and we can go and fetch her.'

'You're going back then?'

'Philip is, I am staying here in England from now on.'

She didn't hide her repugnance at my decision to return without Anna. 'I wouldn't have abandoned *you.*' Her eyes conveyed her anger and her voice was full of venom.

'You didn't have another child to protect. I had to think of Jake as well.'

'Why, where is he? Have you lost him as well?'

'No, no, he is at home with Philip. I didn't want him or Philip to be here when we had this conversation. There are things that happened that Jake doesn't know about and it will make him more unsettled if he finds out.' I paused to let my words sink in. She carried on clearing the kitchen with a great deal of extraneous crashing of pots and cutlery. I thought I would try to move the conversation on. 'Can we have a cup of tea?'

There was no answer but she didn't prevent me putting the kettle on. The tea was made in stony silence. I sat down at the kitchen table and waited for her to calm down sufficiently to join me. I was still uncertain whether another hurricane was about to hit me. Eventually, she grudgingly sat at the opposite end of the table.

I slowly recounted the events of the past few months since Anna had disappeared and also told her of the contributory considerations that had led us to the decision to leave Anna behind. How the airline pilot had wanted to buy Anna, how the man with the broken-down car tried to entice Jake away to buy him a present and indeed, how Jake's friend Patrick had nearly been abducted on the street outside his apartment. I went into huge detail about our searches for Anna in the desert and those by the police and the air rescue pilots. How I had trawled day after day through the souks and back streets of Riyadh looking for her. How we had littered the surrounding villages with posters of her in the hope that someone had seen her. When I told her that Philip had been put into prison, albeit for a short period, she was shocked and astounded.

'Whatever did he do?' she wanted to know. I then relayed the whole rigmarole about the subcontractor being a non-Saudi and then the National Guard discovering that he was a Saudi after all, but only after laying the blame on Philip and putting him under arrest.

'They are all a nest of vipers.' Mum stood and paced around the kitchen in turmoil. 'You are well out of the place.'

'Yes, but we can't cut ourselves off because we need to keep up the search and keep the police searching. We can't let her disappearance drop off their radar.'

By now she had softened her attitude towards me and I approached her carefully. Very lightly I put an arm around her shoulder and was relieved that she didn't shrug me off. I may have been her beloved daughter but I had committed the most heinous crime – I had abandoned her beloved grandchild.

'We will find her,' I said with more confidence than I actually felt. 'Your prayers will be answered.'

'Please God, they will.'

We arranged for her to come to our house to see her precious grandson and Philip as soon as we had been to visit Philip's parents the following day. Another stormy interview.

Philip's mother was already red-eyed before she had answered the doorbell. She said nothing as we went in, overcome with tears. His father strode forward, grim-faced, saying, 'This is a bad, bad business. What's the situation?'

Philip went through the ghastly story again and they looked more and more shocked as he described our distraught searches in the days after the sandstorm. As Philip approached the part when he was sent to prison, I suggested to Jake that we walk down to the shop to buy everyone an ice cream. Elizabeth, my mother-in-law, looked up in surprise but I shook my head at her, indicating not to say anything. Philip could tell them about his jail experience out of Jake's hearing. By the time we got back with a supply of choc ices they were well in the picture and looking anguished. They agreed reluctantly that Jake and I would be best out of possible harm's way and that Philip should stay in Saudi for the time being.

'The future is going to be a trial for all of you,' concluded David, my father-in-law. 'All we can do is hope for the best.'

Conversations with our friends followed along similar lines, although none were as harsh as the one with my mother. Perhaps they thought we shouldn't have left Anna, but none of them knew what it was like living on thin ice, never knowing when disaster would strike again.

It was still school term time in England, so I was able to see the head of my old school and ask him if Jake could rejoin the school in the autumn term. He was very sad that our Arabian venture had come to such a bad end and was happy to admit Jake into the school in September. He also said that one of his staff had told him that she was expecting a baby and would be going on maternity leave at Christmas. Perhaps I would like to apply for her job? This was a very kind suggestion. He must have guessed time would lay very heavily on my hands without work to distract me. I said I would be delighted to apply.

The remainder of Philip's leave passed quickly and before we knew it Jake and I were back at Heathrow to deliver Philip to the doleful sounds of the Imam on the Saudia plane. Check-in was full of travellers heading back to Riyadh. I was so glad not to be joining them, for the time being. We had booked late August flights for Jake and me to fly via Cairo to Riyadh for just two weeks; we were assured that we could get entry visas from AAC's London agent and hopefully, for the return exit visas, the visa official wouldn't need the passports to prop up his wobbly desk.

We kissed Philip goodbye. 'Keep safe and find Anna,' I said.

He smiled ruefully. 'I'll try.'

Summer passed pleasantly. My mother came to see us so often that I suggested she move in until our late August visit to Saudi. She and I tackled the garden which had been neglected in our absence. We would sit on a bench with a reviving cup of tea and invariably talk about our missing girl. It was good I had someone to cry with.

Far too soon, the date of the visit to Saudi arrived. I didn't pack much; the weather would still be hot there so we'd get by with T-shirts and shorts for Jake and the same for me if we went into the desert and, otherwise, long skirts and my abaya for moving around Riyadh. The journey was fairly uneventful except that Jake and I had enough time on our stopover to visit the Cairo Museum to view the treasures of Tutankhamun.

We stashed our suitcases into the left-luggage depository and caught a taxi to Tahira Square by the Nile. I was beginning to feel an old hand at travelling around Cairo. The Cairo Museum was a large imposing red building built in 1902. The government of that time had suffered the loss of several previous museums and had decided to build a splendid new one that would house its wealth of artefacts from antiquity. Even though, for some inexplicable reason, the 1855 government had handed over the *entire* contents of their museum to the Archduke Maximilian of Austria! (Those treasures can now be seen in the Kunsthistorisches Museum in Vienna.) Whatever shortages there may be in Egypt, ancient artefacts are not a consideration. They were able to fill the museum with a new supply of Pharaonic household goods, especially when King Tutankhamun's tomb was discovered in 1922.

Walking through the museum, it reminded me of a warehouse of old bric-a-brac and unwanted household effects. Dilapidated beds, chairs and tables were in a haphazard arrangement along the dusty corridors. The museum was seriously in need of a makeover. We walked into the room holding King Tutankhamun's gold mask with huge anticipation. There it was in all its magnificent beauty! It lay in the centre of a small room with a queue of respectful visitors regarding it in awe. I was very alarmed to see an armed soldier standing nearby in a corner. The mask, made from eleven kilogrammes of solid gold, was far too heavy to run off with but was within touching distance. Perhaps he had orders to shoot if anyone got too near? I held Jake firmly by the hand.

That evening we touched down in Riyadh after another internal flight from Dhahran. There was no invitation to visit the cockpit and no sight of the pilot who had propositioned me. The temperature was stiflingly hot in Riyadh, as it was in our villa, even though Philip had had the air conditioning chugging away day and night. There had been one significant change to our home: Hani had agreed that Philip could keep the villa but our dining room had been converted into a third bedroom so that another of Philip's colleagues could move in with him. The children's bedroom was still kept for their exclusive use. It so happened that Philip's new housemate was on leave so we didn't actually meet him.

Philip managed to avoid a site visit during our stay and we saw more of him than we otherwise would. Even so, it wasn't much of a fun visit. I recommenced my wanderings around various parts of the city with a hot and bothered son in tow. Walking was only possible in the late afternoons and we always needed to be home by sunset. Our police inspector welcomed me in a friendly manner and regretfully informed me that they still had no intelligence as to where Anna might be. I touched base with the embassy to remind them that one of Her Britannic Majesty's citizens was still missing. They assured me that representations to the authorities were ongoing and we would be told of any developments.

Jake's school chums were mainly in England on leave, so play dates were not possible. However, John and Becky had already returned from a trip to Australia and invited us for day visits to their compound. Angelo had forgone his annual leave and had taken the airfare instead to be sent home to his family. Such dedication. He was delighted to see us again and took us over to the Al Akariya compound whilst Philip joined us for an evening dip in the pool and a barbecue before we returned home.

John and Becky said Anna's abduction had had a salutary effect on the expat community. Everyone was far more watchful over their children and felt even more repressed and restricted. They assured us that everyone was looking out for her.

We left Saudi just short of a year since we first arrived. What a lot I had gone through in that time. I was still in my thirties and resilient enough to soldier on. I just prayed that our calamities were over and that we had positive and happier times ahead.

Life goes on

What is the secret of living with a great sorrow? You just keep on keeping on. Mundane daily tasks have to be carried out. Children have to be fed. Husbands have to be supported and cared for. Gradually, the pain recedes, provided nobody mentions it. When they do, the wound opens, and you are swept once more into heartbreaking grief. You are never more than a few words away from being plunged back into the pit. You drag yourself out and recover until the next time.

Jake quickly fitted back into the routine of his old school and I busied myself applying for teaching posts, including the one at Jake's school. Even though it would probably be only temporary, it would be very convenient. The governors appointed me to the staff for the following January but since the pregnant teacher found working during the last month or so of her pregnancy difficult, I joined the staff early as a supply teacher.

Philip was granted two weeks of leave over Christmas and even had his airfares paid since he was going to have to interview potential new staff whilst he was home. I was grateful that we didn't have to return to Saudi and could leave our next visit until the Easter holidays.

This new existence carried on until the following summer when Philip and I had to decide whether he should come home permanently or carry on for another year. Jake was missing his dad and so was I. We were still a young couple and should have been enjoying family life and a mutually satisfying relationship. Instead, I was almost living the life of a widow and he a semi-detached bachelor. The decision was made for us at the beginning of Philip's summer leave when, during an early morning cuddle, Philip noticed a lump in my breast.

I was so surprised to see it, sticking out underneath my breast nestling next to my ribcage.

'Good Heavens!' I exclaimed. 'How could I have missed it?' I spent a horrible few hours until I could get an appointment at my local surgery. My doctor took one look at it and immediately rang the oncology clinic at our local hospital. After a brief conversation he said, 'They want to see you tomorrow morning at 10am.'

I walked to the hospital on a fine sunny day with a cloud of doom hanging over me. *This*, I said to myself, *is the third disaster. Bad things come in threes. I am going to die.* The surgeon prodded around the lump and said it was unusual for it to be growing out of the breast rather than within it. However, it did mean that it was spotted early and could be dealt with promptly. 'What are you doing next Saturday morning?' he enquired.

'I rather suspect I am going to have an operation,' I replied. 'What will it involve?'

'I shall perform a "lumpectomy" which isn't the correct medical term but it describes what will happen quite accurately. We shall remove the lump and send it away for analysis to see if it is malignant.'

'Then what?'

'We'll have a better idea after the operation and when the results come back. They won't take long – it's all done on site.'

We stood and shook hands. 'Fine, we'll see you bright and early next Saturday. Speak to my assistant in the office and she'll tell you what to bring and how to prepare yourself.'

I looked puzzled.

'No eating from the previous evening. No worrying, either. You're in good hands.'

'Well?' asked Philip when I arrived home. Ensuring Jake was not listening, I told him what the surgeon had said. 'Are they optimistic?' he asked.

'Well, they're as cheerful as they can be without actually promising me a long and healthy life,' I replied. 'We shan't know fully until the result of the biopsy is sent back.'

We both sat and pondered the ramifications of what could happen.

As tears began to trickle I whispered, 'I don't want to die without seeing Anna again.'

Philip hugged me and said, 'It'll work out fine. Promise.'

My mother was deeply upset by the news. 'It was only to be expected after all the trouble you've had,' she gnomically pronounced.

'Well, I didn't expect it!' I retorted.

'What will you do?'

'What, if I die? Not a lot.' I was slightly irritated by her assumption that I was on my way out.

However, since Anna had been abducted and Philip imprisoned, she had every reason for pessimism. 'We've caught the lump, whatever it is, very early and the doctors will know very soon what action to take, so don't get too despondent just yet,' I cautioned her.

'I'll pray for you. The Good Lord will answer our prayers.'

I said, 'Thanks, Mum,' as I gave her a hug.

The operation went well and the surgeon said he was very hopeful. The tumour was completely enclosed and there were no signs that it had begun to spread. He would contact me as soon as he had the results.

On the way home from the hospital Philip said, 'I'm going back to Riyadh but only to clear my desk, hand over the project and pack up the villa. We have got to start living again like a normal family – well, as normal as we can.'

Neither of us mentioned the obvious caveats to this decision. It was going to be a momentous step to finally cut our ties to Saudi and, hopefully, I would be alive to do it.

A few days later I had a phone call from the surgeon's secretary to ask me to see him at the end of the week. I thought this a little odd. Why didn't he tell me straight away that I was clear of any problems? On the other hand, he didn't want to see me immediately.

My surgeon greeted me on the Friday morning noncommittally. This felt bad.

'I'm afraid I must tell you that your tumour was malignant.' I didn't respond. I felt I had just been given a death sentence. 'I know it seems bad but we can do a lot for you to make sure you stay cancer free.' I still didn't respond. I didn't know what to say.

'I had to perform a similar operation last year and the patient is fine now. I'll go back into the same area and take away a portion of the surrounding tissue. If there has been any spread we can hopefully remove it. Then you can have a course of radiotherapy to mop up any stray malignant cells.'

'When?'

'Probably in a couple of weeks or so.'

'In a couple of weeks! I could have cancer rampaging through my body by then!' I exclaimed.

He laughed and replied, 'No, no, it doesn't travel that fast. And we have already removed the main source of the malignancy. I'll check my lists for the coming weeks and fit you in as soon as I can.' He sounded reassuring so I thanked him, somewhat despondently, and gave him a crooked smile.

Philip had to return to Riyadh before my second operation but my mother moved back to our house to care for Jake whilst I was being fixed. This was a process that could be dealt with. There was a satisfactory end in sight and I just had to submit myself to the treatment and get through it.

Radiotherapy turned out to be relatively pain-free except that the radiologist always tuned the in-house sound system to BBC Radio 2 and I had to endure weekly sessions of Jimmy Young's perky sense of humour and his bland selection of music. For the following few months, I was strictly warned not to go into the sunshine since the skin exposed to the radiotherapy waves would be particularly vulnerable to being sunburned. However, late summer in England is rarely sunny and being sunburned could be easily avoided. I was able to start teaching at the beginning of term but was allowed to take radiation days off. It made one surprisingly tired.

My brief encounter with the Grim Reaper concentrated my mind and I began to consider ways in which I might one day locate my daughter. Searching for her in Saudi Arabia had proved to be exhaustingly futile. If we had been fluent Arab speakers with close contacts within the Saudi community, we might have stood a chance. If the police couldn't find her there was little prospect of us doing so. I had to assume that she was still alive and had been passed on to a family wealthy enough to have paid for her. If that was the case, then sooner or later she would come to England. The odds of this happening were less than winning the Lottery, but people did win the Lottery and some long-lost children did eventually reappear. Huge numbers of Saudis visited London annually and increasingly large numbers of them bought homes in the more affluent boroughs of Kensington, Knightsbridge and Chelsea. For some reason that was not immediately clear to me, there were always large numbers of Arabs along the Edgware Road, just around the corner from Marble Arch.

I decided that if Anna was to be located anywhere on a visit to England, it would be in West London. I resolved to haunt these areas in the coming years. If nothing else, it would make me feel that I was *doing* something rather than passively hoping that somebody somewhere would do the right thing.

Once a month, and occasionally more often, I would make my excuses to Philip and take myself to London for the day. Eventually, he became curious as to why I went so often on my own. Pleading interest in 'such and such' an art exhibition or opera performance began to sound flimsy excuses. Besides, Philip would often want to come with me and have to be fobbed off. I was safe going to see an opera since he found it a bafflingly weird art form. But there were only so many operas one could see. Eventually I had to come clean and confess to my hopelessly optimistic strategy.

He smiled sympathetically and put his arms around me. 'If it makes you feel better about our impotence and inability to find her, then go ahead. You know it is probably not going to produce results but we are both living in hope.'

Over the coming months and years, I came to know the Royal Boroughs of Kensington and Chelsea, Knightsbridge, Belgravia, not to mention the Edgware Road, as well as I knew the back streets of Riyadh. The staff of Harvey Nichols and Harrods looked at me as if they were thinking, *You look familiar.* I hoped they wouldn't think I was intent on shoplifting since I rarely bought anything. The place I always zoned in on was Harrods toy department. Knowing my daughter's fondness for Hello Kitty merchandise and anything else at the kitsch end of the toy spectrum I thought she might persuade her new 'parents' to take her there. Harrods had some very expensive toys but also a surprising amount of glittery tat. They also had a range of dressing-up clothes which would entrance any young girl – princesses, fairies and flamenco frocks in a range of vibrant colours. Hmmm. She would like them.

We took Jake and a friend to visit Whipsnade Zoo on one occasion and came across a Saudi family admiring the camels. Needless to say, I closely scrutinised the children in the party. I decided that the zoo should be added to my list of places to visit and London Zoo as well. Jake was always keen to come with me. Like both of his parents he enjoyed drawing so I turned the visits into drawing lessons. We became quite accomplished at producing fairly accurate depictions of the animals.

I frequently passed by the Saudi Arabian Embassy in Belgrave Square. I recollected the 'mass' interview I had attended when trying to get a teaching job at the Madrassa. The chaotic visa office in the basement operated for a number of years before moving to other premises as, eventually, did the embassy itself. The double and treble parking outside always made me smile. The drivers in their large black limousines wearing vaguely sinister dark glasses knew they were immune from being booked for parking offences. Most cars bore *Corps Diplomatique* badges. The drivers of those cars that didn't have CD plates worked for people who thought nothing of running up parking tickets like the rest of us buy bus tickets. It was just one of the many expenses of living in London that they could well afford.

Over the years, I noticed more and more Arabs in the streets, driving top-of-the range cars and presumably living in the expensive houses in that area. There were always plenty of well-heeled Middle Eastern guests milling around the Carlton Tower Hotel in Cadogan Place where I sometimes treated myself to a coffee. The local shops were predominantly high-end outlets for Fendi, Dior, Versace, Bulgari and the like. The wealth created by Gulf oil was pouring into the area and Saudi women were only too happy to clothe themselves in ostentatious raiment and festoon glittery baubles about their bodies. It was what Mrs Thatcher called the 'trickle-down factor'. The rich splurge their money and the less well-off make expensive stuff to feed their demand. A friend of my acquaintance worked at a high-end emporium. A request came in for matching plaid dog coats which they didn't make. However, they had plenty of plaid of the desired design to hand, so two coats were manufactured. 'How much?' enquired the delighted dog owner. Everyone in the office looked at each other and someone suggested £3,000 per coat. The dog owner was delighted and so were they!

The Edgware Road catered for a different class of Arab. Not so much the wealthy citizens from the Arabian Gulf, but the flotsam and jetsam that sought refuge after periodic paroxysms of unrest in the Middle East. After chatting to various shopkeepers in the area, I gleaned that migrants had come to the area as long ago as the late 1800s but most had arrived after the 1950s and subsequent Middle Eastern unrest. It seemed unlikely that Anna would be found in this area but it was an interesting neighbourhood to explore.

The change from Oxford Street to Edgware Road was startling. One moment you were in a bustling shopping street similar to one in any major city in the country but, rounding the corner by Marble Arch, it suddenly looked like Cairo. In fact, it is colloquially known as Little Cairo. Women were veiled and dressed in figure-enveloping garments whilst the men also wore clothes more often seen in Egypt. There were numerous hookah cafes with men sitting around tables puffing away at their *shishas*. Shops had signs and advertisements in Arabic and sold newspapers from all over the Levant. There was an ample choice of restaurants catering for Turkish, Lebanese and Egyptian tastes. I noted with interest a *shawarma* restaurant which I resolved to introduce to Philip and Jake – we had developed an appreciation of Middle Eastern cuisine in our time in Riyadh. Not all of our memories were bad.

The Foundling

MEETINGS WITH COUSIN FAISAL'S BRANCH OF the family were not frequent until I was about twelve, when we moved back to Riyadh. By then he was at university studying to be a doctor but he was often the subject of discussion amongst the family. Aunt Salma made no secret of her intention that one day he would be her son-in-law. Amal would smirk at me on these occasions. Her resentment of me had got worse, if that was possible, since my scooter ride down the mountain.

'I can't think how Aunt Noura and Uncle Hammad are going to find a husband for you,' she would explain with false concern. 'Nobody in the family would want you – they wouldn't know what sort of family you came from. Not a nice family, anyway. Not if they could just dump you like

*they did.' I had heard enough of her snide remarks to become
hardened to them and I just shrugged my shoulders.*

'Perhaps I will have to find one for myself,' I surmised.

*'Oh no, Uncle Hammad would never let you do that.
That's not the Saudi way of doing things. You will just have
to stay at home and wither away.'*

*'No, I shall be a teacher and will love being with cheerful
young students who want to learn.'*

*'Well, that won't be good enough for me!' she remarked
as she flounced off.*

*My parents sent me to the best girls' school in Riyadh
and were gratified that I worked hard and showed aptitude
in mathematics. They approved of my ambition to teach and
even encouraged me to think of going to university. I would
be the first woman in the family to go. My math teacher was
English and took an interest in my development. It was she
who first put the idea in my head that I should study math
in Riyadh for my first degree and then go to England for
a Postgraduate Certificate in Education. She had been to
Homerton College in Cambridge and thought that it would
be a good place for me to study. I had somehow to convince
my parents that this was not a step too far. They were
already under some disapproval from the rest of the family
for their encouragement of my educational aims. I would
enlist the help of my math teacher when the time came and
I certainly needed it. Whilst studying for my math degree I
discovered that I had to apply to Homerton College a year
before I intended to go there and that the college would have
to be assured that my English was good enough. Fortunately,
I was able to sit my Cambridge Proficiency exam at the*

British Council in Riyadh, although I would have to go to the college itself for an interview. Thanks be to Allah that I had been on summer courses in Switzerland to improve my language skills. Getting into the college was going to be tough.

Life for women in Saudi Arabia is far more constrained than in other countries, or, at least, Western countries. We have a 'guardianship system' whereby a woman must always have a male guardian to protect and guide her. In practice, it means that you have no control over your life. Your guardian is usually your father but it can be your brother or, amazingly, even your son. Without your guardian's permission you cannot get a passport, travel outside the Kingdom or get married. You need to be escorted when leaving the house, even to go to the doctor. Some of my friends complain bitterly about their lack of freedom and one was even beaten by her brother who had seen her at a print shop by herself where she had wanted to print out her college essay.

I am so grateful that I don't have brothers and that my father is quite reasonable. Even so, I try not to cause my parents trouble.

I secured a place at the King Saud University in Riyadh on the women's campus; the women-only university would have been freer in some respects but the qualifications of the lecturers are generally not as high as those in men's universities. Since men and women are completely segregated I had to attend open lectures by video link. Besides studying mathematics, I also studied Islam which has given me a new insight into my religion. When fundamentalist scholars *say 'so and so' is the law, we women scholars can point out that there is no such stricture in the Koran. Nowhere in the Koran does it say that women may not drive a car. For that matter, it does not say that men can!*

I was able to persuade Ummi to start a course in child welfare at a women's college in Riyadh. My father was somewhat taken aback at this suggestion but when he was assured that his home would be run as efficiently as ever, he agreed. Aunt Salma thought it was complete nonsense and could not understand why she would want to do it. I kept in touch with my school math teacher and invited her for visits to our villa when my parents were there. Gradually they gained confidence in her opinions, which were respectful of our Saudi way of doing things. She spoke with enthusiasm of her time at Homerton College, emphasising how for most of its history it had been a female-only establishment and women students had their own accommodation. She somehow forgot to tell my parents that the college was now co-educational and that I would be studying with young men. Most of all, she thought my job prospects would be enhanced if I was the proud holder of a certificate from Cambridge University. The Saudi Government was giving out bursaries and scholarships for students to study abroad so, it was likely that it would be cost-free to my parents. The drip, drip, drip of propaganda for my educational ambition wore down my parents' reservations. Except one: who would be my guardian?

Padua

ARCHIE AND JENNY STAYED ON IN RIYADH and kindly took on the role of being our local 'eyes and ears'. They periodically visited the police station and also the British Embassy. There was never any new news. I carried on with my perambulations around Knightsbridge and Belgravia. I watched with amusement the blacked-over Saudi women squatting on the pavements outside Harrods waiting for their drivers. I felt like telling them, 'I can do that!'

But Philip and I had to carry on with no indication from any source that the situation would improve. We carried our sorrow in our hearts and only the heavy sigh that expired from either one of us would indicate that we had been thinking of Anna. The pain gnawed away at us and neither of us was far away from brimming eyes.

It would only take a compassionate arm around my shoulder from a friend who knew the situation to make me well up. I could cope as long as no one mentioned her. Occasionally people would only have to say, 'How are Jake and Anna doing?' for my composure to disintegrate. I gradually learned to fob them off and not say anything specific.

The years passed and Jake grew into a fine young man. He was mad keen on sport, particularly hockey, so Philip and I often spent the winter weekends ferrying him around to different schools for interschool hockey matches. When he was invited one Easter to go on a week's hockey tour of northern schools, Philip and I took advantage of his absence to make a tour of our own – around the Veneto, Venice's hinterland, to see the Palladian villas and churches. Being an architect, Philip was a great admirer of Andrea Palladio and I was all for a spot of culture accompanied by lovely Italian food and wine.

Our hotel, La Calcino, was a small comfortable *pensione* on the quayside of the Giudecca Canal, within walking distance of the rest of Venice and near a *vaporetto* stop from where we could quickly motor along the Grand Canal to the Piazzale Roma which sounds romantic but is, in fact, a huge bus station. There we could hire a car for a few days to transport us around the Veneto. Our hotel served breakfast on a pontoon, attached to the quayside outside the hotel. It was magical sitting by the open water with views towards Giudecca Island and, a short distance away, Il Redentore, a Palladian church which was first on our list of must-see buildings. Not so magical were the passing cruise ships on their way to their parking bay at Tronchetto. Floating apartment blocks drifted by whilst their passengers waved down to us, no doubt inspecting our breakfast menu.

Il Redentore is, in the words of the guidebook, a masterpiece of harmony and proportion. The Venetians built the church to Palladio's design, in grateful thanks for the ending of the 1576 plague. Unfortunately, we missed the annual procession to the church, reached via a concocted bridge of connected small boats over the Canal. The interior is so restrained and visually perfect, not cluttered with Baroque accretions which afflict so many churches of that period. We then took the *vaporetto* to the Piazzale Roma and looked in amazed admiration at the Palazzi along the Grand Canal, surely one of the most glorious journeys that one can make by municipal transport. Many of the Palazzi were the town houses of the nobility who owned the Palladian villas we were about to visit. The important business of hiring a car for the following day was somehow achieved (neither of us could speak much Italian and the staff of the hire-car firm didn't speak any English).

We congratulated ourselves with a glass of wine and then slowly made our way back down the Canal stopping frequently at the stations *en route*. It was all so atmospheric. Even the scruffy *sotto paggiata*, passages that wound their way under and around other buildings, somehow looked aesthetically pleasing.

The next morning, we collected our small Fiat and drove over the connecting bridge that links Venice with the horrors of Mestre, the industrial hub of the region. A short drive took us to the Villa Foscari by the Brenta Canal. This Palladian villa has been called the most perfect of them all, but by the end of the week I concluded that each one was *the* most perfect villa. The Villa Foscari is more often known as La Malcontenta, the Unhappy One, after one of its former lady residents was locked up there due to her lack of interest in her marital duties. However, there is some justification for the villa itself to be considered malcontent since an industrial site has grown up around it and the villa had suffered consequent pollution and corrosion of the villa's fabric. The wonderful frescoes that enhanced the interior had suffered and needed expensive restoration.

We pressed on to Padua, where we planned to have lunch and a leisurely stroll around the ancient streets. I took on the role of navigator on this leg of the journey and, as I was checking the road map, the penny dropped.

'We're going to Padua!' I exclaimed.

'You don't say,' replied Philip. 'Glad your map-reading is up to the challenge.'

'No, I've just realised that we are going to Padua where Saint Anthony came from!'

'And?' replied my baffled husband.

'Saint Anthony is the excellent Patron Saint of Lost Things who keeps finding my keys for me. And more. I ought to pop into his church and say thank you.'

Philip looked sideways at me but said nothing.

'It won't take long,' I assured him. 'You don't have to come.'

'I shall take the alternative option of a cup of coffee and select an appetising lunch,' decided my driver.

We parked our Fiat near the city centre and made our way to the Piazza del Duomo, where the domed and minareted Basilica di Sant'Antonio towered over the surrounding buildings. At the café opposite, I asked Philip to order me a coffee and an *insalata caprese* then walked over to the cathedral entrance past a magnificent sculpture of a soldier mounted on a dynamic-looking horse. Subsequent investigation enlightened me that the sculpture was by Donatello and the rider was a mercenary with the improbable name of *Gattamelata* – 'Honey Cat'! Underneath this statue were several barrows containing long candles for sale. This was unusual. Normally, votive candles look like tea-lights and are stacked beneath the candle-stands beside the statue of whatever saint one wished to beg for a favour. I had never seen so many and so long. This should have warned me what I was about to encounter.

Just inside the main door there began a queue which stretched down the central aisle and then veered to the left. This 'pop-in' visit was going to take far longer than expected. I slowly moved forward with the other people, mainly women, who casually chatted to each other, firmly grasping their candles. I gradually became aware that somewhere ahead, somebody was in difficulty. I could hear crying but my neighbours seemed unconcerned and carried on talking quietly. As we approached a prominent side chapel on the left, the crying became louder and there was also wailing from another source. It became obvious that I was approaching the tomb of Saint Anthony and that the pilgrims were giving vent to their grief. The altar was placed at the top of a flight of stairs but the pilgrims slowly moved around the back of the raised area. The women in front of and to the side of me were now in an anguished state. There were small children's shoes and gloves and articles of clothing propped up on the plinth, whilst below, bereft mothers pleaded to the saint to find their child or return them to good health, many of them pressing photographs to the wall of the back of the tomb. Initially, I felt completely out of my depth at this display of emotion. To thank Saint Anthony for finding my lost keys (and once a 'cello bow) seemed trite and flippant. Then I knew what to do. I pulled out my passport photo of Anna that I always carried with me, pressed it to the back of the tomb and whispered, 'Dear Saint Anthony, please find Anna for me.'

The current of grievers moved on and I rejoined them. The supplicants then went over to the vast array of lit candles, where I touched the tip of mine to another lit candle and placed it with the hundreds of others. Everyone slowly filed out through another entrance, gradually recovering their equilibrium. Thank goodness I had dark sunglasses with me and thank God Philip had opted for the coffee alternative. He couldn't have coped with the unrestrained display of misery.

'Hello,' he said when I finally appeared at the café, 'that took a long time.' Looking at me carefully he said, 'You OK?'

'You'll never believe what I've just witnessed.' I described the whole amazing event and began to well up again when I got to the pressing-of-the photo part.

'God, it sounds awful. Couldn't you get away?'

'I didn't try. I asked Saint Anthony to find Anna. If anyone can, he can.'

Philip held his counsel on the subject. We carried on with lunch and I ordered another coffee.

Later, on our way to Vicenza, I brought up the subject again.

'The thing is, with Saint Anthony, you can't just hand your problem over to him and say, "Get on with it." You have to keep looking. Keep searching. Don't give up.'

'So, you're going on with your wanderings around London?' asked Philip.

'Yes, but wherever I go, I always hope she'll be there. We might even find her in Vicenza!'

Philip laughed. 'That would be good.'

Vicenza is a lovely old city. Bathed in afternoon light the ancient stone buildings, roofed in red terracotta tiles, represent quintessentially Veneto architecture. Not grandiose but dignified by its centuries of existence. However, the basilica displays a roof in a fetching shade of green. Surrounding the building is a magnificent covered walkway or *loggia* designed by the city's most famous son, Andrea Palladio. He must have had a heavy workload. Not only are there beautiful villas all over the Veneto but there are also churches and even the oldest surviving indoor theatre, the Teatro Olimpico, in his home town.

The theatre is closely influenced by the structure of the Odeon Jake and I had visited at the base of the Acropolis in Athens. Tiered seating, appearing to be made of stone is, in fact, made from wood. Since it is an enclosed theatre it has a ceiling but it is painted as if there is a blue sky above. It would have been marvellous to hear a concert there.

On our way back to our car we called in at the Museo Civico in the Palazzo Chiericati, which has one of the most astonishing painted ceilings. It is yet another Palladio building although the ceiling fresco was painted by one of his many collaborators, Giulio Carpione. Across the ceiling is the underneath view of a passing chariot, just glimpsed as it tears across the sky. Most arresting is the depiction of the charioteer's nether region, naked. The preliminary studies for this painting must have been interesting to witness…

It was evening by the time we reached the avenue of trees approaching Mestre. There was a considerable number of young women standing casually in small clumps beneath the trees, dressed in Hollywood Hooker outfits – high heels, short skirts and plunging necklines. They mostly adorned themselves with extravagant bouffant hairstyles and lashings of make-up. I was surprised to see so many of them and astonished that numerous police cars were parked amongst them, with policemen propped up against their vehicles chatting with the 'working girls'. They didn't seem to be at all interested in moving them on.

It would have been terribly off-putting to the punters to have to proposition the hookers with the police watching on. But perhaps the girls felt safer knowing that the police were keeping an eye on the transactions.

The following day, we drove north from Venice to Treviso and then on to the fortified town of Castelfranco where we stopped for a coffee. We were heading for the nearby Villa Emo, which we didn't think we would be able to visit since it was still the home of the Emo family. However, as we gazed up at the splendid entrance through the heavy iron gates, a minibus arrived with a party of American students. Their leader was an architectural historian who had been given permission to take his party around the villa. He was happy for us to tag along with his group so we surprisingly gained access to this stunning house. The wealth of the Emo family had derived from the fertile lands of the estate and its plentiful supply of water. This had led them to cultivate maize for which they could get a higher price than the sorghum previously grown. In acknowledgement of this source of their wealth, floral arrangements of corn cobs from the previous harvest welcomed visitors on the *piano nobile*, the raised main floor of the villa. We climbed the grand entrance steps, that were more like a ramp so shallow were the risers, to the porticoed entrance, and admired the surrounding parkland.

Inside, the frescoed walls were wondrous to behold. People seemed to be toppling out of balconies to the salon below! It was difficult to tell what was real and what had been painted.

Later, at the Villa Barbaro near Maser, we were similarly intrigued by the portraits of the inhabitants who appeared to be coming through doors to greet us or were casually leaning over high balconies to see who had just arrived.

I suddenly found my heart was racing and I came out in a cold sweat. Something had alarmed my senses but I couldn't see what it could be. Philip was at the far end of the vast room which was otherwise empty. I slowly rotated to see what had triggered the sensation. I gasped to see a small girl looking very like Anna coming through a door. However, the door and the child had been painted several hundred years previously. I was rooted to the spot and stared at her until my brain assimilated that she was one of the many lifelike depictions. I was still acutely aware of small dark-haired girls, even though my own girl would have been a teenager by then.

'Amazing paintings,' said Philip as he joined me. He then noticed the child coming through the door and gasped, 'My God, she looks just like Anna.'

'Yes,' I agreed, 'I was taken aback for a moment or two.' We both smiled affectionately at her and left. I hoped that this was an omen that Saint Anthony was on the case.

The artist Paolo Veronese, who had collaborated with Palladio on the construction of the villa, had the ability to create *trompe l'oeil* down to a fine art. *Trompe coeur* as well.

We finished our trip to Venice with two days of being regular tourists, soaking in the atmosphere and visiting a few galleries. On the first day the weather was cooler than it had been, so I wore my Jaeger coat and carried my new plaid Burberry bag, thinking I appeared an unusually stylish tourist. Nevertheless, I had an extraordinary encounter with an Italian gent. Philip and I were approaching the Rialto Bridge when Philip spotted a public convenience under a nearby portico.

'I'll just pop in there. Can you wait?' Just for a change, I didn't need to go so took myself to one side, out of the way of the stream of people climbing the steps to the bridge. He was away longer than I had anticipated so I propped myself against a column, folded my arms and surveyed the passing crowd. Yes, I was certainly better dressed than most. An Italian chap interrupted my thoughts by asking, '*Quanto fa pagare?*' It took a moment or two to understand that he was asking, 'How much do you charge?'

I was indignantly affronted. 'I'm English!' I replied, not that my nationality had anything to do with his proposition, but it was the first thing that came to mind. He held up his hands saying, '*Oh, scusi,*' then disappeared into the crowd. Philip came out of the toilet and noted my cross expression. 'You OK?' he asked.

'Philip, do I look like a prostitute?'

He appraised my appearance and replied, 'Well, maybe an expensive one!' and skipped sharpishly up the steps before I could handbag him.

Although my head was spinning with having seen so many treasures of art and architecture, my mind often returned to my impromptu pilgrimage to Saint Anthony's shrine. If he was to find my girl, then I was going to have to persevere in my searching. Whatever else the visit might achieve, it had put new vigour into my resolve to find her.

The Foundling

I WOULD BE ABOUT TWENTY-TWO BY THE TIME I STARTED
my postgraduate course and still had to be under the
guardianship of a male relative. (My parents assumed
that I was about three years old when they adopted me and
that my birthday was the day that I arrived. No one knows my
real birth date.) Being in England made this easier said than
done. Ummi and Abi mulled over this problem at length. I
kept out of their discussions waiting for them to arrive at the
obvious conclusion. Eventually, my mother said, 'What about
Faisal?! Isn't he in England now studying to be an eye surgeon in
London? Opthalmolo-something or other. I can't pronounce it.'

'Ophthalmology. He is training to be an ophthalmologist,'
helped my father.

'Yes, an eye surgeon. Such a clever boy, Alhamdulillah
(Praise be to Allah).'

227

'He might be too busy.'

'You could ask him.'

'I will write to him tomorrow,' agreed my father. Nobody asked me, which was just as well. I kept my head down in my book so that they wouldn't notice my flushed cheeks and wide smile.

Faisal wrote back to Abi saying he was indeed busy but would be happy to be available to advise me and to keep a brotherly eye on me.

I met Faisal briefly in the summer whilst Ummi and I were in Montreux. Strictly speaking, we shouldn't have had contact with each other since we were both unmarried adults, but since he was going to be my guardian we had to renew our relationship. We were chaperoned by Ummi – she felt reassured that propriety was being observed even if we were going to be unchaperoned when in England. We just kept to the rules to keep her happy.

Whilst Ummi was out of hearing Faisal said that he would be able to 'keep a very close eye on me' since he was going to be researching into infectious diseases at the hospital in Cambridge. He said this with a smile so I knew he was going to be supportive but undertake his guardian duties with a light rein.

Cambridge was unbelievably green. The tree-lined roads that led to the college shaded pedestrians from the autumn sun. Girls wore shockingly few clothes – shorts or skimpy skirts and vest-like T-shirts. But they didn't flaunt themselves – they just seemed to take it for granted that no one would find it remarkable. I got rid of my black outer clothing and wore lighter colours. I still covered my body and hair but tried to fit in. The other girls were friendly and showed me around the college. Whenever a group walked into the city centre they invited me with them but as weeks passed they acquired cycles and I had to walk alone or catch a bus. One fellow student, Rana, was from Bahrain, so we struck up a particular friendship. She had a bicycle and said she would teach me how to ride it. For quite a while I kept my distance from the young men at the college. It took me several weeks to conquer my shyness and talk to them as naturally as Rana did.

My guardian rang me in my second week and suggested that we go for a walk on his day off. He lived with a fellow doctor in a flat near to the hospital and not far from my college. He met me by the college front gates and we headed down a tree-lined avenue until we came to a field with grazing cows which was nearly in the centre of the city! Extraordinary! We crossed the field, or fen, as I learned to call it, manoeuvred our way past the cows and avoiding the cowpats. People cycled past, ringing their bells at the cows and us, chatting away to each other as their hair and clothes billowed out behind them.

'My friend Rana says she'll teach me how to ride a cycle,' I informed Faisal.

'Without my permission?' he replied.

I shot him a startled look but he was laughing at my dismay.

'I'm only joking. It's a very good idea, especially in Cambridge. It's flat so it is easy to get about. Where we are going this afternoon, they hire out cycles. Would you like to have a go?' I was wearing trousers under a knee-length shift so my clothing wasn't an impediment.

Once I had been equipped with a cycle and helmet, we walked across the grass to a path and stuffed my bag and Faisal's jacket into the basket ready for lift-off. Or wobble-off. It was hard work for Faisal to keep me upright and, eventually, to get me going by running along beside me holding onto the saddle.

'Hannah, I need a rest!' he gasped. I needed one too. We sat by a children's paddling pool and ate ice creams. I watched the mothers and children splashing in the pool and men with their friends kicking a ball about. It was all so relaxed.

'Different to home, hey?' said Faisal.

'I am not yet comfortable with seeing men and women mixing so freely.'

'Yes, it is a bit of a shock at first. But you'll get used to it.'

We took the cycle back to the hire shop and set off on our walk to Grantchester which, over the coming weeks, became our favourite walk. Faisal was very easy to talk to. He told me of his plans to train as an eye surgeon so that when he returned to Saudi he could help the many people who were affected with eye problems. Apparently, many people in desert countries suffer from trachoma. This disease easily spreads in unhygienic conditions, not only from person to person but on flies that carry the infection from face to face. I was used to seeing the vans driving around Riyadh in the early morning spraying the air to kill flies that would otherwise make our lives a misery. Garbage collectors took rubbish from houses every morning to further prevent flies from breeding. Our government was taking measures to improve the people's health.

Faisal was actually in Cambridge to research *Cytomegalovirus* – CMV – which is an infectious disease which can affect eyesight in people whose immune system is suppressed. He was investigating how the immune system reacts to CMV. I could imagine that Amal would be enthralled with this piece of intelligence. He was to be awarded a Master of Philosophy degree from Cambridge University although I was baffled why a scientist would get a degree in Philosophy. I hoped my certificate would be in Education and not in Business Administration! Cambridge could be opaque at times.

I talked with enthusiasm about my plans to be a teacher, how I wanted to have a role in the future of my country and to have some say in the way that I lived.

'You are lucky you have supportive parents,' remarked Faisal. Neither of us mentioned that, at some point in the future, I would need a supportive husband.

My course kept me busy. Not only did we have seminars and workshops on how to teach, but teaching practice was integrated into the course throughout the year. At first, I found it nerve-wracking going into school, but the pupils were keen to learn and I think they liked being taught by young enthusiastic students. Some of the pupils could be disruptive and it took all my ingenuity to keep them interested in what I was teaching. I wasn't used to dealing with teenage boys, in fact I had hardly ever met one outside of my family. I found the best way to keep the pupils engaged was to keep them busy and praise their efforts whenever I saw positive behaviour. Praise to a student is like water and sunshine on a plant.

Whenever Faisal had free time that coincided with mine we went out together exploring the city or the countryside around. We walked and walked and talked and talked. He was the perfect elder brother. In my heart I would have liked more – but I knew that he was committed to Amal and I resolved to be grateful for this interlude with him.

Rana and I spent a lot of time discussing our college work and how we might be able to fit in with the education system back home. Bahrain was much more liberal than Saudi – she could even drive a car there – but we would have to adapt what we were learning to a different system. Perhaps we could influence that system to be more child-centred and lead to a more investigative approach, away from rote learning. We had lots of ideas.

One evening, we were watching television in the common room when I saw a programme that was to change my life. It was about hypnosis – something I knew nothing about. A hypnotherapist had hypnotised a woman and was slowly taking her back into her past. It was amazing to watch the woman, who was German, gradually change her demeanour from a confident adult to that of a wary, uncertain child. At one point she stopped understanding English and the rest of the session had to be conducted in German. She curled up on her chair and sucked her thumb. Eventually, the therapist could go back no further since the woman/child could not understand any language.

'I would like to do that,' I told Rana.

'Become a hypnotherapist?'

'No, be taken back into my early life and find out where I came from.'

Rana looked stunned. 'Why, what happened to you?'

I explained that my early life was a mystery. My parents could not or would not explain where I had come from. I was not their natural child but I had possibly come from an English family.

I made my mind up to find a hypnotherapist who could help me.

Finding one was surprisingly easy. There were several in the Yellow Pages *so I selected a therapist who operated in a clinic not far from the college. I made an appointment for a consultation and on the following day called in to put the therapist in the picture. Ophelia Fitzpatrick was a tall, elegant woman with a calm and friendly approach. She said she thought she could help me and did not object when I said I wanted my friend Rana to be present and that Rana would be videoing the session. I then went into town and bought a small video camera and spent the rest of the day with Rana learning how to use it.*

The hypnotherapy session was later in the week. Rana set up the camera on a stand ready to start filming and was then free to help with translating, should I revert to speaking only Arabic, like the German woman in the television programme.

Looking at the session later, it seemed I was gently led into a deeper and deeper level of relaxation when my mind was almost in a dream-like state. The process of regression took the form of movement down a long mental corridor where different doors opened onto past events in my life. At each open door I could revisit the sensation of being in places with people that I had long forgotten. We eventually reached the time when I was newly with my Saudi parents and I became visibly uneasy and bewildered. I was still speaking English to Ophelia but describing an environment which was distressing. Later, I found it difficult viewing. I then continued along the corridor to the next door through which I remembered a sandstorm where all was confusion, noise and fear. I called out 'Mummy!' and 'Daddy!' repeatedly and cried piteously. Watching it later, Rana held my hand and comforted me. Further back in time I was happy and cheerful. The sensation of my earlier life was of a positive environment with my parents, my real parents. Ophelia asked me what I remembered and I could see the faces of my mother and father and my brother. His name, Jake, came to mind. I saw us in our house where we had a white cat and lots of kittens. I saw a smashed glass table which I had somehow broken. When Ophelia asked where I came from before Saudi I answered, 'Arstin.'

'Where is Arstin? Is it near another town?'

I thought for a while before answering, 'Camrij.'

'Cambridge?' asked Ophelia.

'Yes!' I replied.

'Did you go there?'

'Yes,' I replied. 'Mummy got me some flower earrings. They hurt!'

The session came to an end with me feeling at peace with my early life. As I came out of the trance-like state I felt contented and calm.

'Goodness me!' exclaimed Rana on our way back to college. 'That was amazing. Can you remember much about it?'

'Yes, I think so, but it will be interesting to watch the video. Did I actually say I lived near Cambridge?'

'Yes!' exclaimed Rana. 'Perhaps your parents are here? Perhaps you can find them?'

My mind was in turmoil, knowing that my real parents might be living within easy reach of my college. But I had no idea where to find them and couldn't locate Arstin.

At our next meeting, Faisal suggested that we might like to visit Hatfield House which was a short drive south of Cambridge. I discovered that the house was not a house but a beautiful 400-year-old palace. Another example of British understatement. As we left Cambridge we passed through a village which I scarcely noted, but its name, Harston, rang bells.

'Faisal, I think I have been here before!' He slowed down as I scanned the houses but nothing looked familiar. Towards the end of the village there was a turning. 'Please, go down there, Faisal.' He did, but was looking at me questioningly.

'How can you know this place?' he asked.

As we drove down the street I recognised the shape of the street, its curves, trees and houses. The last house was a small cottage, which, with a rush of delighted emotion, I recognised as my very own home. I had seen this house in dreams and had no idea why it had appeared to me in my sleep. It was so small! But it still had a yellow front door and the brick steps where I had sat watching my daddy paint it. I could hardly speak but eventually whispered, 'This was once my home.'

'How do you know?'

I took a deep breath and told him of my visit to the hypnotherapist.

'Without my permission!' he chided me but, nevertheless, looked suitably impressed. He listened intently to my story and how I guessed that Arstin was in fact Harston. And sure enough, here in front of us was the house that I remembered.

'Do you think your parents still live here?'

I shook with excitement at the very thought. The nerves in my face prickled and a hot, clammy sensation swept over me. Could they be here?

We tentatively rang the doorbell and a young woman answered. She did not know who had lived in the house twenty years previously but suggested we spoke to the neighbour over the road. This time the door was answered by an elderly woman who eyed us suspiciously. Yes, she could remember the family who had lived in the cottage but they had moved to the Middle East. They sold the cottage and she had no idea where they were now.

'What were their names?' I asked.

'Thomas. Mr and Mrs Thomas.'

For the rest of the day I was very quiet, my mind in turmoil. Where were they? Somewhere in Cambridge, somewhere in Riyadh? How could I track them down?

Faisal was concerned and sympathetic. He also warned me that finding my real parents would cause considerable *apprehension to my Saudi parents. He suggested that we keep our discovery to ourselves for the time being.*

Faisal was ending his research project in Cambridge and was shortly due to resume being a doctor at the Riyadh Eye Hospital. I was very miserable at the prospect of us not being able to continue our friendship but kept up a cheerful appearance. I didn't want his memories of me to be of a dull, pathetic creature. We had a last meal together when we discussed everything, except what we hoped would be our personal futures. I didn't want to hear about Amal and he didn't enquire about my intentions regarding marriage.

We shook hands and he briefly kissed my forehead.

I went back to college and cried.

Rana and I completed our teaching course and became proud owners of Certificates in Education from Cambridge University. We vowed to keep in touch and hopefully visit each other.

My last few days in the calm greenery of Cambridge were blown asunder by a highly excited call from my mother in Riyadh.

'It's happened!' she shouted down the phone. 'Faisal is going to marry Amal! Your Aunt Salma is floating on air!' She went on and on about the coming wedding and I said nothing. Eventually she asked if I was still there. 'Isn't it wonderful news?!'

'Yes,' I replied. 'Terrific.' Apparently, Faisal's and Amal's fathers had been discussing the suitability of the marriage and concluded that a marriage between the cousins would be highly beneficial to all concerned.

My nine months in Cambridge had been eventful. I had gained a highly regarded qualification, located the place where I came from, though not yet my birth parents, and had made two valued friends. One I would see regularly in the coming years and the other hardly ever.

I stopped off at Montreux on my return to Riyadh to meet up with my mother. To my huge irritation, Aunt Salma and Amal were there as well. It was wedding, wedding, non-stop wedding. Where would the ceremony take place, what would Amal wear, where would she buy the gown? I clamped my teeth together and made the semblance of a smile. Eventually Amal noticed I was not as delighted as she thought I ought to be about her coming nuptials.

'Aren't you pleased about my wedding, Hannah?' she enquired.

'Thrilled,' I lied. But there was one thing I was interested to know. 'When did Faisal propose to you?'

*'Propose to me! Of course he didn't **propose** to me. Our families arranged it. That's what we **do** in Saudi. You've been away too long, you ninny.'*

'So, you haven't talked to Faisal about the wedding?'

'There's plenty of time for that,' she responded with an airy gesture.

She was about to leave the room but suddenly stopped and turned. 'You saw Faisal in England.' It was more of an accusation than a question.

'From time to time. He was very busy.'

'Did he talk about me?'

'No, we didn't talk about personal matters.' Amal seemed mollified by this response.

She then left to look at jewellery and dress shops with Aunt Salma. I declined to accompany them. Somehow, I got through the week without smacking her. I took myself off to Verbier for a day, saying that I was going to Montreux to look for math books at the bookshop in the town centre. Nobody wanted to come with me. I travelled by train and then took a cable car up to Les Ruinettes on the lower slope of Mont Gelé and made my way to the cycle station. Feeling free of family encumbrances and disapproval I hired a scooter and helmet to repeat the descent that I had experienced as a child. I had several months of cycling in Cambridge to give me confidence but, if I fell and broke my neck, too bad.

I went down quite slowly but nevertheless felt the exhilaration of the speed and the freedom of doing something outside my comfort zone.

Back in Riyadh I prepared myself for my future career. I had already approached the British International School who had said that I could spend my probationary year with them, teaching math to the older students. Before he left Riyadh for his annual leave in England, the head of the math department had left me the school's math syllabus to study.

As I was working my way through it one morning, I heard the front gate bell ring and saw our gateman open the gate – to Faisal! Whatever was he doing at our house? My mother came bustling into my room with the exciting news. 'Faisal is here! I expect he has come to invite us to the wedding.'

She looked at me with irritation. 'Oh do try to show some interest in Amal's wedding.' She threw up her hands and departed for the kitchen. We would have to wait some while to find out what the men had been discussing.

After an hour or so my father came into my room, looking strangely out of sorts. 'Please, Hannah, go down to the garden, Faisal wants to speak to you.' I felt my face go crimson. I went to the bathroom to splash water on me, comb my hair and gain a sense of equilibrium. I loosely wrapped a white veil over my hair.

Faisal smiled at me in welcome. 'Hi, Cousin!' he said.

'Hello, Faisal. I wasn't expecting to see you so soon.' We wandered over to the bench beneath the gazebo and sat at either end of it.

After a considerable silence he said, 'Hannah, you would make me the happiest of men if we could be married.'

'You are going to marry Amal!' I shot back.

'No, I am not. She is the last person I would want to marry.'

'Oh, she's not that bad,' I replied magnanimously.

'She is very nice but I am a doctor and know enough about consanguineous marriages to avoid one like the plague. We are too closely related. I want a wife who can give me healthy children.'

One moment I was elated, the next I felt completely deflated.

*'Oh, so you want to marry me because I am **not** your cousin! How very convenient for you. We are, for all intents and purposes, cousins but you and I know that we are not.'*

Faisal shuffled along the bench towards me and took my hand saying, 'Dearest Hannah, this conversation has not gone the way I intended it to. We have got to know each other very well over the past few months – far better than we could have done under normal circumstances.'

I kept my face severely expressionless and let him explain away the apparent cynicism of his proposal.

'I thought you a lively and adventurous child when we rode down the mountain together. That is why I was happy to be your guardian in Cambridge. We have talked many times about our hopes and expectations and I have grown to respect your opinions and your desire to help our country. I have also fallen in love with you. I kept my distance from you in Cambridge because I did not want anything to impede my decision, my hope, that one day we would be married – if you accepted me. Do you think you could love me?'

I could keep it up no longer. 'Yes!' I exclaimed and kissed him on his lips, disregarding what my watching parents would say. He kissed me back and disregarded them too.

'I have loved you from the time you took me down the mountain,' I confided to him. 'I thought you were destined to marry Amal so never let myself hope for anything more than friendship. Why did Aunt Selma think you were going to marry Amal?'

Faisal sighed and recounted the ferocious arguments he had had with his father. The two fathers had decided that Faisal and Amal were a suitable match and hadn't expected opposition from Faisal. His father is a doctor and could understand the objections on health grounds. He had seen the misery of the early deaths of my parents' sons and gradually conceded that Faisal had a point. Marrying me was keeping the family ties close but without the danger of close genetic inbreeding. Eventually Faisal had convinced his father that I was a suitable match and left his father to disentangle the arrangement with Amal's father.

Needless to say, my mother was deliriously happy, Aunt Salma was livid and Amal was incandescent with rage.

We married only two months later and our son, Ya'cub, a fine healthy child, was born early the following summer. We named him after my brother, Jake. Ya'cub means Jacob which is Jake's real name.

This is the end of my story, so far. Much has happened in my relatively short life and I am wondering what new surprises await me.

To be continued, insha'allah…!

Once more, once less...

I LOST COUNT OF THE TRIPS I MADE TO WEST London over subsequent years. I usually combined visits to the great emporiums of Knightsbridge with visits to the V&A or the Science Museum or architectural gems such as Leighton House.

The day I found Anna was initially no different from those of any of my previous visits. I was wandering around Harrods and had made my way through children's wear, marvelling at the confections of lace and embroidery as well as the astronomical cost of them. From there I casually perused the evening gowns of Room 7 and, yet again, declined the assistant's offer of help. I then called in to the cloakroom near the department selling electronics and technology and checked the time. Would I catch the 4pm train home or eat nearby at Zia Teresa and catch a later train after the rush hour? In most departments there were Arab women completely veiled over, wandering about following their husbands or in small groups of family members. As it was then twenty-four years since I had last seen my daughter, I was now looking for a young woman, probably of my height and colouring. But if she was swathed head to toe in black veil and abaya, it would take more than a casual glance to recognise her.

I left the cloakroom and paid a visit to the toy department, noting a clutch of Arab women at the far end. As I slowly made my way towards them my eye was caught by a display of Hello Kitty merchandise. I smiled to myself in fond memory of the frequent visits to the shop next to the Euro Marché supermarket in Riyadh where Anna loved to visit. I knelt down to examine some umbrellas, and selected one, not unlike the one that got me through the ear-piercing debacle. Someone else was taking it from the other side of the display. I apologised and stood up. I smiled at the black-veiled woman and caught my breath. She didn't have dark liquid brown eyes but pale green ones, just like my mother. We stood staring at each other. All I could see of her face were her eyes but she could see all of my face.

'Anna?' I whispered. She stared hard at me for several moments.

'Mama?' she replied.

I held onto the display with an iron grip as my head swirled in a vortex of emotional turmoil.

As I steadied myself I said, 'Anna? Is it you?'

She came to her senses quicker than I did and said, 'Go to the comfort room through there,' indicating the one

I had just left. As I went in, the attendant walked out. I went to the end around the corner where we would be out of sight of anyone casually glancing in and waited. I felt angry with myself for letting her out of my sight but she followed me a few minutes later and we went into one of the toilet stalls.

As she removed her face veil I found I was looking at a younger version of myself.

Out of sight of anyone I took her dear face in my hands and looked at her familiar tear-stained features through my tear-blurred eyes.

'I've been looking for you from the moment we lost you,' I whispered.

'In that horrible sandstorm.'

'Yes. You remember it?'

'Always. I couldn't find you!'

'We need to go somewhere we can talk. Can you get away?'

'I can tell my family I need to go to another department and will catch up with them later.'

'Make your way down the escalator and leave the store by Exit 10. You'll be in Hans Road. Cross over to an Italian restaurant called Zia Teresa. You'll see it from the exit. I'll wait for you there.' She repeated my instructions to herself then gave me a lovely smile.

'I'll be there soon, promise.'

I hovered by the cloakroom door, watching her weave through the department towards the women at the far end. She had a short conversation with them then turned back in my direction. I moved quickly to the escalator and made my way down to Exit 10 and crossed the road to the restaurant. It was almost empty but still serving food. After checking that I could take a table, I sat by the front window watching the exit to see when she emerged. As she glanced over to the restaurant I waved and only moments later we found ourselves sitting side by side towards the back of the establishment. She removed her veil again and I took in her face, marking the changes that had occurred over the intervening years. There was a close resemblance to me but also a strong likeness to Philip.

'Do you mind removing your veil in public?' I asked.

She laughed. 'No, not at all. I only have it on because I am with my husband's mother. She is rather conservative and it is easier to please her when we are out together.'

'You are married? Is he kind to you?'

She put a reassuring hand on mine, so like her father. 'Yes, he is. He is a modern Saudi – we both are!'

The waiter came over to take our order. I turned to Anna. 'How long have you got? Do you have time to eat?'

She consulted her watch and considered. 'I'm fine for an hour but I shall be eating later. Perhaps just a coffee.'

I ordered two coffees for us and a salad for me. I was going to be catching the post-rush-hour train and would need some sustenance. I was still holding her hand, hardly believing it was all real. It was difficult to know where to start; how much did she remember of the days after the sandstorm? Did she live with her new family straight away? Who are they? Why didn't they hand her over to the police? The questions just poured out of me.

She just wanted to know why we didn't find her. 'I remember crying a lot. I wanted my mummy and daddy. My new parents were very kind and little by little, I stopped being so frightened.' We both cried a lot during the conversation. In fact, I didn't really stop the whole hour we were together.

'What is your name in Arabic?'

'Hannah. That is the nearest name to Anna. That was the only name I answered to. And look!' She pulled back her head veil and her long chestnut hair to reveal gold ear studs in the shape of flowers. They were still there!

'I wouldn't let anyone remove them. I remembered when you had them put in and you gave me the red umbrella because it hurt so much. I thought if anyone touched them it would hurt again. It was a way of remembering my old life.'

'I was afraid you wouldn't remember your old family – you were so very young.'

She recounted what she could remember, which was more than I expected. She recalled going somewhere on a camel with me and Jake, walking through the desert with the family, being given a doll with a pretty dress. Of England, she surprised me by telling me that she knew she was from a small village not far from Cambridge. I was astounded.

'However did you remember that?'

She smiled and said, 'It's a long story. I will tell you when we have more time.'

She had only vague recollections of our faces although, when she saw my face in the toy department, distant

247

memories surfaced. I then pulled out of my bag the photo of her that I always carried with me. She smiled when I showed her the passport photo that had been reproduced on so many flyers.

'Do you have photos of Daddy and Jake?'

'No, but I will next time!'

She then proudly showed me two photographs: one of a handsome Saudi in thobe and headdress, her husband, Faisal, and a young boy who was a dead ringer for his mother.

'Your son? What is his name?'

'Ya'cub, it means Jacob.'

'That's Jake's full name! Jake is short for Jacob!'

'Yes, I knew that.'

I wanted to ask her if she could get away from her Saudi life and come back to us but I could see by the loving way she looked at her husband and son that there was no hope of that. All that I ever wanted was to find her and bring her home. Now, I had found her – but the prospect of her return was evaporating in front of me.

I told her about the months of searching around Riyadh and the outlying villages. Also, how upset we all were when we eventually left Saudi.

'Why were you in Harrods?' she asked. I explained my thinking and how I hoped that one day I would bump into her. It was such an improbable hope but it was all I had.

'I am so happy you kept on looking for me.'

'But you can't come back to us?' I had to make sure.

She placed her hand on my arm and smiled. 'I am a Saudi now. I have a family and a job and a life in Riyadh.'

She understandingly said nothing as I wiped away more tears.

Eventually, she said, 'But now we have been reunited, we can meet every time I am in London.'

I wanted to know what her family's reaction would be. She said she would speak to her husband first and between them work out a strategy. His family would probably be more welcoming than her adoptive parents. Her family would be fearful that Philip and I would accuse them of stealing her.

'I'm afraid I would want to accuse them of more than that!'

Anna held my hand and looked directly into my eyes. 'We cannot rewrite the past, Mama. We shall all have to reconcile ourselves to what has happened if we are to go forward. Don't make enemies of my parents. They gave me a happy childhood.'

I had to acknowledge that I had prayed for that over the years. I had just wanted her to be well cared for and to be happy.

Anna suddenly remembered the time and said she would have to hurry back to her parents-in-law's home in The Little Boltons.

'Can we meet tomorrow?' I asked with a degree of desperation. 'Your father and Jake will be filled with joy when I tell them. Philip can come with me to London tomorrow. Jake works in South London so will be able to come too.'

'I have a dental appointment on the South Bank tomorrow at 11am. Can you meet me in the lobby of the

Marriott Hotel? I will think up some excuse to be on my own for the afternoon.'

'Are Faisal and Ya'cub with you?'

'No, they are at home in Riyadh so I can do what I like without too many questions.'

We exchanged mobile phone numbers and kissed goodbye.

Walking back to the station I was barely conscious of where I was or where I was going.

I wanted to shout out, 'I found her!' I beamed at every passer-by. The glum, preoccupied passengers on the underground received the full radiance of my happiness. Some smiled back nervously whilst others looked away fearfully in case I was about to launch into an unwanted conversation. I was desperate to talk to Philip and Jake and give them the news we had always longed for.

Reunion

WAITING AT KING'S CROSS STATION I HAD A CUP of coffee and made some important phone calls. 'Hi, it's me. I am catching the 7.15.'

'OK, see you in an hour.'

'I've found her.'

Silence. 'What?'

'I found Anna. I've found our girl.'

'When? How?'

'In the toy department of Harrods. I really have found her.'

There was a choking noise at the other end of the line. When Philip eventually spoke, his voice was thick with emotion. 'Did you speak to her?'

'Yes! For an hour. You are going to meet her tomorrow.' Then I choked up as well.

'This is unbelievable! How did it happen?'

Through my clogged-up voice I managed to say, 'I'll tell you all about it when I get home. In the meantime put the champagne in the fridge. I am going to ring Jake now. He'll want to be there as well.'

But my next call was to our old friends David and Tina who owned a *pied à terre* in Parliament View, an apartment block, a ten-minute walk from the Marriott Hotel. David answered the phone. After the normal pleasantries I asked if we could use their apartment for an afternoon family meeting the following day. He said that we certainly could and to speak to the porter on arrival to get the keys. He would ring straight away to let PV know we were coming.

I then rang Jake. 'Hi, Mum. Had a good day in London?'

I couldn't actually speak for a moment or two. 'Hi, Mum?'

'I've found Anna,' I croaked.

It was his turn to be dumbfounded. 'Did you say you'd found Anna? Christ! How? Where? Are you sure it was her?'

'Yes, we spoke for an hour or so. We have arranged to meet again tomorrow. Your dad and I are meeting her in David and Tina's flat in Parliament View. Can you be there, say, one o'clock?'

'Wild horses couldn't stop me. But tell me how it happened.'

I told him I would ring him later when I got home and would fill him in with the delightful details of our extraordinary encounter.

Philip was almost hopping up and down with excitement when I met him by the front door.

We hugged and grinned and jigged around the hall. With a glass of champagne in my hand I gave as coherent an account of my meeting with Anna as was possible, given that I wanted to tell him everything in as short a time as possible. We spent the rest of the evening and well into the night talking about the encounter, what she looked like, what had happened to her over the intervening years and how we should approach her given that we were essentially strangers to her and that, having been brought up a Saudi, she might have reservations about being with a strange man, even though he was her father. What wonderful dilemmas to solve!

Jake was thrilled with the news and marvelled that I had happened to 'bump into her'. Yes, it was a marvel, but it had come about from unremitting faith that sooner or later, our paths would cross. And great good fortune.

The following morning, we stocked up with food and drinks from the rail station's Marks & Spencer for our lunchtime meeting. They were packed into our rucksack for easy carriage to Parliament View; Philip was to go straight there and open up the apartment whilst I waited at the Marriott Hotel for Anna to appear. I texted her with a short cryptic message: 'Marriott when you're free. What time?' I didn't know who might be looking at her phone, so I kept the message brief. She texted me back a short time later: '12 noon. Are we staying there?'

'No,' I replied, 'have fixed up a private venue 10 mins away.' I would have added a happy smiley but didn't know how to do it. How amazing! I was actually texting my lovely girl.

I sat outside the hotel drinking my coffee and gazing at the imposing architecture. The inner courtyard of the old County Hall is a mighty construction. Huge columns hold up arches over the entrance whilst a grand staircase leads to the main vestibule. In fact, the whole building was a proud response to the Houses of Parliament opposite. 'This,' it proclaimed, 'is the heart of the greatest city in the world. You run the country, but we run London!' Except of course, it no longer did. Mrs Thatcher had bitterly resented the power of the politicians across the water and eventually the Greater London Council was abolished. The building was bought by a Japanese entertainment company, becoming the repository of a hotel, various fastfood outlets and obligatory tourist attractions. And the home to a family of starlings! Earlier, as I stood by the front wall of County Hall watching queues of tourists waiting to travel on the London Eye, I became aware of loud chirruping from a nearby air vent. Out popped a starling which collected a piece of food, dropped by a passing eater, and promptly returned to the vent to feed its family! I suppose it was a lovely hidey-hole. They were safe from scavenging rats but had a good supply of food.

From my vantage point in the inner courtyard, I saw Anna coming towards me, this time dressed in a knee-length shift over silk trousers. Around her head was a light-coloured scarf but her face was unveiled. We both beamed at each other.

We kissed and she asked, 'Where is Daddy?'

'He is waiting, very impatiently, at our friends' flat which they have lent to us for the afternoon. It's a ten-minute walk away. Is that OK?'

'Sure. I love to walk in London. I have so little opportunity to walk in Riyadh.'

We were quickly onto the subject of getting around Riyadh and comparing what it was like when I was searching for her and what it was like now. We concluded that the Saudi summer heat was impossible. As we walked by St Thomas's Hospital I asked her, 'Do you remember what your English surname is?'

'I believe it is Thomas. I am, was, Anna Thomas.'

'My goodness! You have a phenomenal memory.'

She smiled enigmatically.

'I am already remembering things I had forgotten. I am sure more memories will come back to me.'

'I have brought a stack of photographs of the family with me. I doubt you will recognise anyone.' I stopped to show her a photo of Philip – I thought she ought to see how he looked now. She looked at the photo intently matching his new face to the one she vaguely remembered. 'Yes, I sort of remember his face. Perhaps when we meet there will be a greater likeness to the one in my mind!'

'Well, you haven't got long to wait.' I glanced up to the array of windows of Parliament View and spotted Philip looking down to us. 'There he is, there's your daddy!'

Only minutes later we were in the flat and Philip greeted his darling child. Without hesitation she held out her arms and Philip enclosed her in his. We all smiled at each other through red-rimmed eyes and brushed away the tears.

In a choked voice Philip said, 'You used to say, "Daddy, I lub oo berry muts." I've missed you saying that to me.'

'Yes, I think I remember saying it!'

We stood for a while and surveyed the wonderful view across the Thames towards the Houses of Parliament, resplendent in the afternoon sunshine with windows and gold pennants glinting at us. There was enough breeze to make the Union Jack flap with enthusiasm. The water traffic chugged up and down the river whilst above, on Lambeth Bridge, there was a constant stream of cars, trucks and red buses rushing past.

A few months earlier we had borrowed the flat for an overnight stay. Arriving at school later in the morning, I couldn't help bragging, 'I saw Big Ben from my bed this morning!'

One of my colleagues quipped, 'Is that what Phil calls it?!'

There were so many shrieks of laughter that my attempts to explain that I really *had* seen the famous clock tower were drowned out. I wouldn't be sharing *that* particular memory with Anna.

We then sat either side of her on the sofa asking her about her life and family and telling her how we had fared in the years since she was taken from us.

She had grown up with her new family who did not have any other children. Philip and I glanced meaningfully at each other at this piece of news. Her aunts and uncles lived in Riyadh so there were always plenty of children around until they moved to Jeddah. She was educated firstly in Jeddah and then, on the family's return to Riyadh, at a private girls' school, and studied mathematics at the women's department of Riyadh University.

'I enjoyed maths at school!' said Philip approvingly. 'What have you done with it?'

'I went to Homerton College in Cambridge to get my qualification as a teacher and I am now teaching math at a school in Riyadh – I have a nanny who helps me look after Ya'cub.'

I must have looked aghast at this information.

'What is the matter?' she asked.

'We live a couple of miles from the college! You were so near to us and we never knew! Didn't you remember you had lived in Cambridge?'

'It was purely by chance that I went to Homerton College. My math teacher in Riyadh had been there and suggested I went there to study for my teaching diploma. Whilst I was in Cambridge I went to a hypnotherapist,' we both gasped at this piece of information, 'and went through a process of regression which takes you back through your life and helps you to remember your past.'

'Good Heavens!' I exclaimed.

'I remembered more from my early years than I ever knew was locked away in my memory. Quite by chance I one day found myself in Harston.'

Philip and I both exclaimed, 'Harston!'

'And I knew I had been there before. I saw the old cottage where we had lived but the neighbour didn't know where you had moved to. She said you were Mr and Mrs Thomas. So, I had a lot of help with my memory.'

We were all stunned by this news and stupefied by the missed chances that we had been oblivious to.

'The one thing I don't know is exactly how old I am or the date I was born,' continued Anna.

She was amused to discover she was actually six months older than she thought she was and that her birthday was several months after the date of her disappearance.

'If you come to England in July we can organise a birthday party for you!'

She said she would like that very much.

'My husband is an ophthalmologist, an eye surgeon – many in his family are doctors. His father owns and runs a clinic.'

'When you were little, we took you to the Riyadh Eye Hospital. Does he work there?'

'Yes, how strange. Why was I there?'

'Jake threw a paper dart at you in the back of our car. Point blank range. The dart went into your eye and cut the cornea. He was in bad trouble for doing that.'

'Where is Jake?' she asked.

I glanced at my watch. 'He'll be here shortly. You won't recognise him.' I gave her Jake's photo.

'Good gracious!' she exclaimed. 'So dark! He's very good looking.'

'Yes, we have produced two very attractive children!'

Anna laughed and stared at Jake's photo. Despite being white blond when she last saw him, he was now more of a Mediterranean colouring. When he was a teenager his hair went darker and darker. He had strong symmetrical facial features and, if he had grown a moustache and worn a thobe and ghutra, could have passed as an Arab.

'What does he do?'

Philip explained, 'He studied product design at university and now runs his own sports equipment company.'

Right on cue, the doorbell rang. I let him in and as he surveyed his long-lost sister he threw caution to the wind saying, 'Hi, sis!' and gave her a bear-like hug. We all laughed but she took this embrace from a stranger with aplomb.

Over a picnic lunch we exchanged family information and gradually a degree of informality crept in. She was intrigued by photographs of her grandparents. She could remember my mother and being hugged by her. 'Granddad used to give me a tube of Smarties!' she suddenly recalled.

'Do you mind if I look at the back of your neck?' I asked. She looked mystified but nevertheless shyly removed her headscarf. At the base of her skull was a red birthmark, exactly the same as the one on her grandmother's neck. She had never seen it or knew it was there. 'You have your granny's fingernails as well,' I said as I took her hand and showed them to Philip. She was our girl, alright.

Over the course of the meal we tentatively discussed how we could take things forward. She said she would not mention to Faisal's family that she had met us but would speak to him as soon as she returned to Riyadh. The orthodontist had told her that he would fit 'rail-tracks' to her teeth to straighten them in six weeks' time, the earliest she could return to England. I suddenly felt cross with her 'new parents' that they hadn't sorted the problem when she was a child. Her teeth weren't too congested, but Anna hoped some orthodontic work would help. 'Perhaps Faisal can come with me next time and you can meet him?'

'And Ya'cub?' I added.

'*Insha'allah*,' she replied. We all smiled. Yes, if Allah willed it, we would all be fine.

Happy ever after?

WELL, NOT ENTIRELY. OUR DAUGHTER DIDN'T come home to us but at least we knew where she was. Thousands of parents around the world are separated from their children who live across the globe. We just happened to have one who lived in Saudi Arabia.

Our parents were thrilled beyond measure that Anna had been found. 'God has answered our prayers,' my mother intoned in the voice she used when imparting News of Great Importance. And who could argue with her? But I made a silent 'Thank you' to Saint Anthony who possibly had a hand in the miracle. Elizabeth and David cheered and clapped and rushed to open a bottle of bubbly. All three were desperate to see her again but we cautioned them that it might take some time to get her family 'on board' with the turn of events.

Six weeks later, on Anna's return visit to see her orthodontist, a meeting was arranged for us to congregate in the Marriott's Gillray's café after her appointment. Faisal would be there as well. We were more than apprehensive about meeting him since he would heavily influence his wife as to whether the relationship would blossom or not.

Philip and I entered the café and scanned it for son-in-law material. No one fitted the bill so we settled down with a coffee each. Through the window, I eventually spotted Anna with a young man in a suit holding hands with a young boy, our grandson. They entered Gillray's smiling, Anna beaming, but her husband's smile was more circumspect. Little Ya'cub smiled apprehensively. We stood, also smiling in welcome, shook hands with Faisal, kissed his wife on the cheek and ruffled their son's hair.

Faisal was, like most Saudis, tall, dark and of slim build. He wore a well-tailored dark grey suit, brilliant white shirt and conservatively coloured tie. He had the ubiquitous black moustache but was otherwise clean-shaven. Altogether, an attractive man.

Initially, it was an awkward encounter. Anna was friendly, introducing us to her husband and son. Ya'cub was easily won over by a toy we had brought him which he unwrapped and played with whilst we talked. Faisal was pleasant but wary; what, he wanted to know, were we anticipating from this unexpected reconnection with Anna.

I left much of the opening conversation to Philip. He was more in command of his emotions than I was and was able to convey our delight at finding Anna again but also that we recognised that her life was vastly different to what it would have been and that she now had obligations to her family which we would respect. With some difficulty I restrained an impulse to say I wanted as much contact with her as possible. I knew this would kill the relationship stone dead.

'Hannah told me that she went missing in the desert outside Riyadh during a sandstorm?'

'Yes,' replied Philip and once more repeated the sorry saga. The fruitless searches in the desert and later around the streets of the city. The searches by the police including one by helicopter. Our visit to the Governor of Riyadh's *majlis* to ask for help, our visits to the British Embassy. None had produced concrete news of our daughter's whereabouts.

'Do you know how Anna's – Hannah's – parents came by her?' I asked.

Faisal looked uncomfortable. 'Her family and mine are related, distantly, but I do not know the full details. I believe she was given to her parents by other relations where there had been a death in the family. Hannah's parents did not have children so were happy to take care of her.'

I bet they were, I thought to myself. 'Didn't anyone notice she wasn't an Arab?' I could have bitten off my tongue.

After a few moments of embarrassed silence Anna said, 'If you think about the photo you showed me at our first meeting, I *did* look like an Arab child.' She was quite right – she did. I took out the photo from my purse and handed it to Faisal. He smiled as he studied it and glanced down at the living replica, playing with his new truck. 'Yes, she was a beautiful girl. Ya'cub takes after his mother.'

Looking at me, Faisal said, 'You must have been in a living hell.'

'Yes, until six weeks ago, I have nursed a broken heart. Finding her again has been beyond happiness.' Anna and I were now both red-eyed.

'How would you feel meeting Hannah's parents?'

Feel?! The thieving bastards who stole my child! Who deprived us of a happy life with her! Who knowingly took her away from the family who loved her! Feel?! I clamped my teeth together until the rage subsided. Philip, sensing I was about to ruin everything, saved the situation with emollient words: 'We are grateful that Anna had loving and caring parents. We cannot rewrite past events and hope that all of us together will build a future relationship.'

Faisal looked directly at me. 'Kate?'

I took a deep breath and marshalled my thoughts into a positive response. 'Yes, Anna's happiness is all that matters to us. We will do whatever we can to build bridges between her two families.' I somehow conveyed the words without resorting to sarcasm or bitterness.

'Well,' replied Faisal, who was now looking positively cheerful, 'perhaps you would like to meet *my* family? My parents and sisters are in London at the moment. Hannah's family are not here, though.'

Thank God for that, I thought to myself.

'Are you free tomorrow?'

We readily accepted the invitation, even though work in Philip's office would again be disrupted. My school would have to do without me, yet again, but the staff were very supportive and understanding.

The following morning, we travelled back to London and made our way to South Kensington tube station. From there we walked along the Brompton Road to The Little Boltons, where the family owned a London residence. The Little Boltons is not quite so swanky as The Boltons but, nevertheless, is a very desirable address. The Al Murrai house was approached by a flight of steps to the front door, although it wasn't exactly a house, but a three-floor apartment that started on the first floor. We followed the Filipino maid up a wide staircase that opened out into a large reception room. Faisal, Anna and Ya'cub were waiting for us. We were warmly welcomed and seated on ornate chairs not unlike the ones in the Governor's *majlis*. The room was furnished with chairs and tables that looked expensive but not exactly at the cutting edge of design. Two pendant candelabra illuminated the room. The carpets were very beautiful, placed randomly over the parquet flooring.

Ya'cub looked at us shyly and then with pleasure when his grandfather handed over another present. We could hear crockery being moved about in the neighbouring room and surmised that refreshments were on the way.

'You would like some tea or coffee?' asked our host.

'Coffee, please,' we replied in stereo.

At that moment his parents entered bearing trays of cups and saucers and pots of coffee. Plates of *petits fours* were carried by two young women whom I took to be Faisal's sisters. They had gone to some trouble to put on a good show. We stood and greeted everyone in our slightly rusty Arabic: '*Salaam aleikum*' and '*Wa 'aleikum as-salaam*.' The three younger women were unveiled but Faisal's mother had a black veil draped over her hair. We were very new to the family but they had obviously decided that a degree of uncovering was permissible.

All of the Al Murrai family could speak English so we tentatively made conversation with each other. Dr Al Murrai questioned us about where we lived, what we did for a living, how many children we had (thin ice at this point) and why were we in Saudi when Hannah was lost. Having established that we were a family of good standing, he seemed more open to the idea that our families could be connected.

'Hannah has been brought up a good Muslim woman,' he said somewhat pointedly. Philip replied that he had assumed that was the case. 'You have no problem with that?' Well, if we had, we weren't going to admit to it.

Philip explained, 'We have to accept that Hannah has been brought up differently to the way that we would have done it. I am sure that, over time, we shall all get accustomed to our differing viewpoints.' Dr Murrai nodded at this remark but didn't go so far as to agree with it.

All the women had been listening silently so I thought it was about time the ladies had a turn. I turned to Mrs Murrai. 'I love your carpets. Did you bring them from Saudi?'

She was slightly surprised to be addressed but readily joined in. Yes, they had brought the carpets with them but had furnished the house from Harrods. It was nearby and easy to shop there, she explained. I got the impression that she wasn't aware how Anna and I had discovered each other so I changed the subject to Leighton House Museum which was only a few streets away. Had they been there? None of them had so I was able to wax lyrical about the wonderful tiling that had been inspired by Arabian architecture and decoration.

Faisal clapped his hands together and said, 'Why not go today? Kate and Philip, would you like to come to lunch with Hannah and me, and Ya'cub? We could go to Leighton House afterwards?' This seemed a highly suitable way to end the interview; the ice had been broken and we could perhaps have a more relaxed visit the next time.

There was a restaurant nearby serving Middle Eastern cuisine, which suited us all. Seated around the table, Faisal said, 'Sorry about the grilling from my father. We Saudi men are very protective of our women. My father wanted to be sure you would not expect Hannah to change her life if she had regular contact with you.'

'Do you think he was satisfied?'

'Yes – and before you ask, I am too!'

'And you, darling,' I turned to Anna, 'are you happy to be part of our family again?'

'Yes, Mama. We're all going to live happily ever after!'

After lunch we all made our way up to Leighton House to continue our Arabian-themed day. Faisal and Anna were astounded to find a mini Granadan Alhambra cum Sevillean Real Alcazar existing in their Kensington neighbourhood.

'I had no idea there were such lovely examples of Islamic ceramics here in London,' exclaimed Anna. 'I *love* these designs!' she enthused.

'I make ceramic tiles,' I said. 'In fact, I have just made a tiled table based on a wall design in the Alhambra.'

'Really? I'd love to see it.'

'You shall, darling, when you come to visit us.'

Neither of them suggested an early visit so I left the subject to bubble away in their minds. They looked in awe at the intricately decorated Gold-Domed Arab Hall and I heard Faisal tell Anna that he would bring his parents to visit the house. He may well have changed his mind when we climbed to Lord Leighton's studio on the first floor. It had been converted into a gallery exhibiting the artist's paintings, a number of which depicted vaguely clad voluptuous females. Islam prohibits the depiction of the human form, an injunction blithely ignored by the artists of the seventeenth- and eighteenth-century Mughal era in northern India. Their sublime illustrations of courtly life included many intimate portraits. But Lord Leighton's paintings of these naked Victorian women displaying their charms would be deemed offensive to many Muslim viewers.

Without taking a huge interest in the naked women portrayed on the walls around us, Faisal asked, 'Why is Western art so preoccupied by naked figures?'

'Well,' I started, 'artists are interested in conveying the representation of human and animal form. You would think it odd to see animals in art, dressed to cover their modesty. Artists paint the human figure without clothing because that is what we look like. Clothing is often a result of climate; in the jungles of Africa and South America, people wear very little. In northern climates they wear an awful lot. I suppose Arabs, who live in a hot climate, need to cover up to protect themselves from the sun. But, in addition, from historical times, people have adopted religious ideas about modesty to ward off sexual encounters which are frowned on outside marriage.'

'Hmmm,' he answered. 'Interesting. But I can't help feeling there is a prurient element to Western art.'

'Possibly because, formerly, most artists were men and so were the buyers!' I agreed.

'I think you shouldn't show your mother these paintings,' said Anna. 'But your sisters are doctors; they'll be used to seeing naked bodies.'

'You know a lot about art, Kate,' added Faisal.

'Well, a bit,' I replied. 'I teach art so I'm interested in all forms of representation – painting, print, ceramics, sculpture. But there's always something new to discover. I'd like to know more about Islamic calligraphy.'

'Ah, you had better talk to my mother. She is a noted calligrapher.'

'And I would like to talk to *your* mother and *yours*, Daddy,' added Anna. Turning to Faisal, she said, 'Can you do without me this weekend? Perhaps, just me the first time then you and Ya'cub next time?'

'Sure,' he replied. I was glad to see that she could decide things for herself and her husband didn't mind. That was reassuring.

She came to stay at our house the following weekend and slept in the room I had made ready for her after our move to the new house. Her soft toys were propped up on the bed which still had the same bed linen. Her other toys and books were ready for her – though Ya'cub would get more use from them now. Dotted around the room were the various prayer mats that she had been given as a child as we had wandered around the carpet souk. She was surprised to see them, and vaguely remembered being given them. I nearly said, 'You'll be able to use them whilst you're here,' but managed to stop myself in time.

I sat down on her bed next to her and held her hand. 'You know, darling, how very happy we are to have found you. But I have to ask, what has been the reaction of your parents in Riyadh? Have you confronted them with the fact that you were abducted and stolen from us?'

Anna sighed and was silent for some time. Eventually, she replied, 'It is very difficult for them and for me. I love Ummi and Abi. They are my parents who have brought me up, cared for me, loved me. I was very angry with them on my first visit when I returned to Riyadh. I told them I was devastated to discover that I had been stolen from my real family and that they had kept me, knowing how much grief they were causing my real parents. They were shocked to find that I had stumbled upon the truth. Ummi cried and cried. The blood drained from Abi's face knowing that he was shown up to be less honourable than he had held himself to be. He said that they had been suddenly presented with a situation of a small girl, without family, needing someone to care for her. When I asked him how much investigation he had carried out to find out where I had come from, he was silent. It was obvious that I was the answer to Ummi's prayers for a child. They didn't find out because they didn't want to.'

I pressed further, 'Did you ask them if they had paid money for you?'

'No, I didn't ask. If they had, they would not admit to it. It would be too shameful.'

'So, you think they did?'

After a further period of silence Anna said, 'Yes, it is possible.'

'How is your relationship with them now? Do they know you are meeting with us in England?'

'I do not live in their house so I do not have to meet them on a daily basis. I have my own house to run, Ya'cub to look after, my job as a teacher, all taking a lot of time. We have space to get used to the new situation. Things are quite strained but Faisal is very good at keeping us all in contact. It is very hard for me to know that my parents deceived me in such a profound way. But... in time we shall be reconciled.'

There was no point in going any further. Anna was in turmoil with her family in Saudi and it wouldn't benefit the situation for me to add fuel to the fire. However, I knew that Philip and I should avoid, at all costs, meeting Anna's adoptive parents. The conflagration would destroy everything.

Anna's reunion with her grandparents was joyous beyond belief. As she stepped into the sitting room my mother welcomed her with open arms. 'There's grand for you!' she exclaimed. Her Irish accent had largely melded into a Kaymbridge one (not to be confused with a Cambridge accent) but at times of heightened emotion her original accent came to the fore. 'You're a fine strong girl, so you are.' She then gave her finest accolade, 'All the way from Ireland!' Anna looked somewhat mystified by this remark but there was no point in explaining it. She would get used to her nana's oddities soon enough. Mum sat Anna down beside her on the sofa, holding her hand as if to prevent her ever leaving again.

'How are you, Nana?'

'I'm fine! Never better. Thank God He has returned you to us! But your mother tells me you're a Heathen now?'

'No!' Philip and I chorused.

'Anna is a *Muslim*, not a *Heathen*. She worships the same God as you do. Allah is the Arabic name for God.' This was news to Mum who looked puzzled.

'Well, never you mind,' Mum added. 'I'm sure God doesn't mind what you call Him.'

Anna has a sweet nature and she listened to her nana with amused interest. She was thoroughly grilled, yet again, and answered the interrogation with a full explanation of her life.

'Here is my son and husband,' said Anna, proudly handing over her photographs.

'Oh, he is a darlin' boy, a dote. Just the same as his mother. You looked just like that when... when we last saw you.' Anna put her other hand tenderly on her nana's arm.

'And your husband, he's a fine-looking man. Does he have other wives?'

'Mum!' I scolded her. 'You can't ask something like that!'

'No, he doesn't,' answered Anna smiling, 'I think he has his hands full with me!'

Before she could ask any more embarrassing questions Philip's parents arrived. Anna prised herself away from one grandmother and went for a hug from her other one.

'You are so beautiful,' said Elizabeth with tears in her eyes. 'You quite take my breath away.'

'Welcome back, Anna,' said David. 'This is the best thing that has happened to us.' He was unsure whether to kiss her or not so covered his indecision by saying, 'Here, Philip, a bottle of champagne to celebrate.'

'I'll pop it into the fridge,' replied Philip, 'I'm sure Anna won't mind us drinking to her return.' Explaining this odd remark to his father: 'Anna is a Muslim, she doesn't drink alcohol.'

'Don't worry about me, I shall be happy with fruit juice,' added Anna.

David apologised for his mistake, but no offence was taken. In fact, the rest of us toasted our girl with added jollity.

Anna submitted herself to more questioning whilst we all marvelled at how our little girl had grown into this self-assured young woman. She was a credit to her upbringing but – she undoubtedly had good genes…

Epilogue

T O OUR ENORMOUS RELIEF, WE NEVER MET
Anna's adoptive parents. My blood boiled every
time I thought about what they had done to us.
However desperate they were to have a child to love, they
knew what a vile act they had perpetrated in depriving us
of our child. We knew it was in the best interests of the
family's future relationships that we acknowledged Anna's
affection for both sets of parents. We just had to make sure
we never came in contact with them.

In early January of the following year there were
reports in the news of yet another tragedy in Mina, a
suburb of Mecca where Hajj pilgrims performed the final
rite of the Hajj, stoning a wall that represented Satan.
There had been a stampede when vast numbers of people
tried to fling their stones before sunset. Three hundred

and forty-five people were killed and nearly a thousand injured.

Days later we heard that Anna's parents had died in the stampede. Anna and Faisal had decided not to go to Mecca at the last moment since Ya'cub had developed a worrying temperature and they had not wanted to leave him with the nanny.

Praise be to Allah.

Allah moves in a mysterious way
His wonders to perform;
He plants His footsteps in the sea
And rides upon the storm.
(Almost) William Cowper (1731-1800)

About the Author

M S James travelled to Saudi Arabia in her 30s with her husband and children. She worked there as a teacher for five years, firstly in a private Islamic school and then at the British school. On her return to the UK she continued teaching, mainly music and art. She lives in Cambridge.